PRACTISE YOUR

BASIC

Gaby Waters and Nick Cutler

Illustrated by Naomi Reed
Designed by Graham Round
Editor: Lisa Watts

Contents

About this book

This book contains lots of exercises, puzzles and problems to solve by writing programs, to help you practise your BASIC. There are programs with missing lines and variables to fill in, listings full of bugs to spot and correct, and ideas for programs to write yourself. The book covers all the most important BASIC commands, starting with simple PRINT statements and ending with guidelines for writing a long program for a treasure hunt game.

Programs filled with bugs and mistakes are marked with a "bug" like the one at the beginning of this paragraph. This tells you to hunt for the mistakes and correct them so that the program runs properly. Other programs have lines and variables to fill in. The lines you have to complete are marked with an asterisk and the spaces to fill are marked with question marks.

The answers to all the puzzles and program projects are given at the back of the book with detailed explanations. Use the answers to help you when you get stuck especially in the longer programs. Often the answer to a problem in the first few lines can help you solve later problems or give you a hint to writing the rest of the program on your own.

Sometimes the program lines in the answers will differ from the ones you write yourself. If your program runs alright, don't worry, there are often several ways of writing the same program. Try comparing your answers with the ones in the book to see which method is the most effective.

All the programs in this book are written in a standard BASIC which means that they should run without much alteration on most computers. Some words are different on all computers so if you type in a program and get a bug you should check the BASIC words in the program. There is a conversion chart to help you on page 47.

If you are not sure what a BASIC command does, there is a guide to BASIC which lists all the words used in this book and gives a brief explanation of each one. Special guidelines are given for writing programs on Sinclair (Timex) computers and there are also alternative answers for these computers.

3

Getting to know BASIC

These two pages give you some practice using the command PRINT. This tells the computer to display something on the screen. You can use PRINT as a direct command, that is, with no program line number and the computer will carry out the instruction straight away. After a direct command you have to press RETURN (or ENTER or NEWLINE, it varies on different computers).

```
PRINT "FISH"
PRINT "2 FISHES"
PRINT 2345
```

Remember to press RETURN or your computer's word after each command.

```
PRINT 2+2+3
PRINT 6*8
PRINT 15-4
PRINT 16/4
PRINT SQR(16)
PRINT 5346-257
```

Try typing these direct commands into your computer. When you tell the computer to print letters, or letters and numbers together, they must be in quotation marks. Numbers by themselves do not need quotes.

You can also use PRINT to make the computer do calculations. Here are some simple sums using BASIC mathematical symbols. If you are not sure what they mean, try them out.

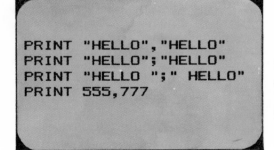

```
PRINT "HELLO","HELLO"
PRINT "HELLO";"HELLO"
PRINT "HELLO ";" HELLO"
PRINT 555,777
```

```
PRINT "       HELLO"
PRINT SPC(10)"HELLO"
PRINT TAB(15);"HELLO"
PRINT TAB(10);555
```

All these instructions tell the computer where to print on the screen. Try them out to see what they do. Punctuation marks have special meanings in BASIC. A comma tells the computer to leave some spaces before printing the next item and a semi-colon tells it to print the next item on the same line without leaving a space.

Correcting mistakes and altering programs

Mistakes in programs are called bugs. They can be caused by simple typing errors, or by breaking the rules of BASIC. You need to find out how to correct mistakes on your computer and how to alter programs.

Most computers have a DELETE or RUBOUT key for correcting mistakes.

ELLO

To insert a missing letter you have to move the cursor. Look in your manual to find out how to use the cursor control keys.

To delete a whole line, type just the line number followed by RETURN (or your computer's word).

Simple program puzzles

Here is a simple program to try. It makes the computer display the message shown on the screen on the right. Try running the program, then see if you can change it to make the screen look like those shown below. The direct commands on the opposite page should help you. There are some hints on altering programs and correcting mistakes at the bottom of the page.

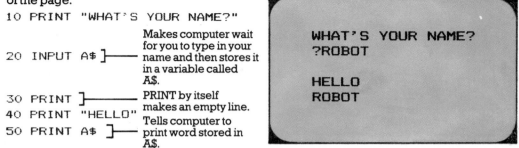

```
10 PRINT "WHAT'S YOUR NAME?"

20 INPUT A$ ]———— Makes computer wait
                   for you to type in your
                   name and then stores it
                   in a variable called
                   A$.

30 PRINT ]———— PRINT by itself
40 PRINT "HELLO" makes an empty line.
                Tells computer to
50 PRINT A$ ]———— print word stored in
                  A$.
```

```
WHAT'S YOUR NAME?
?ROBOT

HELLO
ROBOT
```

Type the program into your computer pressing RETURN (or your computer's word) after each line. At the end, type RUN and then press RETURN.

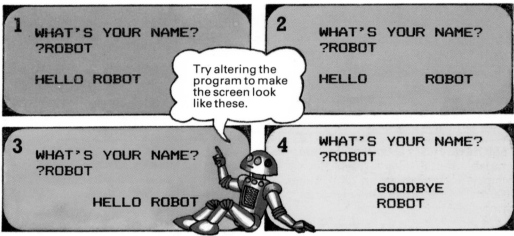

1
```
WHAT'S YOUR NAME?
?ROBOT

HELLO ROBOT
```

Try altering the program to make the screen look like these.

2
```
WHAT'S YOUR NAME?
?ROBOT

HELLO          ROBOT
```

3
```
WHAT'S YOUR NAME?
?ROBOT


          HELLO ROBOT
```

4
```
WHAT'S YOUR NAME?
?ROBOT


          GOODBYE
          ROBOT
```

The difference between the program and the direct commands on the opposite page is that each line of instructions in a program has a number. The computer stores the instructions in its memory and does not carry them out until you type RUN. If you use line numbers going up in tens you can add extra instructions without renumbering the program.

To look at a listing of the program on the screen, type LIST.

To delete a whole program, type NEW.

```
10 PRINT "THIS IS A"
20 PRINT "PROGRAM"
15 PRINT "SILLY"
```

You can add new lines anywhere in a program, or correct old ones by retyping them. Try typing in this program exactly as it is here and see what happens when you run or list it.

Variable puzzles

A variable is a labelled space in the computer's memory where a piece of information is stored. To tell the computer to store a piece of information in a variable, you can use the BASIC words LET or INPUT as shown below. Information containing words or a mixture of letters, numbers and symbols is called a string. A string must be in quotes and its label has a dollar sign after it.

```
10 LET A=16
20 LET R$="RUSTY ROBOTS"
30 PRINT A
40 PRINT R$

RUN
16
RUSTY ROBOTS
```

A and R$ are variable names.

```
10 PRINT "WHAT'S YOUR NAME?"
20 INPUT N$
30 PRINT "HOW OLD ARE YOU?"
40 INPUT A
50 PRINT N$;" IS ";A
```

String variable

LET tells the computer to label a memory space and put some information into it.

INPUT labels a memory space and makes the computer wait for you to type in the information when you run the program.

Choosing variable names

Which of these are legal on your computer?

Some of these variable names contain BASIC words and will make a bug. Which are they?

```
LET B$="6422 RATS"
LET B5=6422
LET K1=99
LET FL$="FLEA"
```

```
LET LETTER$="HI!"
LET TEN=10
LET RUN$="MORE RATS"
LET FLEA$="50 FLEAS"
```

BASIC is very fussy about the label you give a variable and the rules vary on different computers. For instance the ZX81 (Timex 1000) only accepts one letter names for string variables.*

If you use words as variable names you must not use ones which contain BASIC words as this will confuse the computer. Try the lines given above to see which are legal on your computer.

Words and variables

```
10 LET RR$="RUSTY ROBOT"
20 PRINT "HELLO ";RR$
```

Try typing a comma instead of a semi-colon and see what happens.

```
10 LET R$="RUSTY"
20 LET S=66
30 PRINT R$;" ROBOT ATE ";
40 PRINT S;" SAUSAGES"
```

When you put words and variables together in a PRINT statement, the words must be in quotes and you put a semicolon between

PRINT puzzle

```
LET A=66
LET B=77
LET RR$="RUSTY ROBOTS"
```

the words and the variable. You need to leave a space inside the quotes either side of the words. Try leaving out the spaces in the lines above and see what happens.

```
66 RUSTY ROBOTS ATE
77 SINGED SAUSAGES
```

Can you write a program using the variables given above so that when you run

the program your screen looks like this?

*If you have a ZX81 you will have to alter string variable names of more than one letter where they occur in this book.

Looking inside a program

This program converts temperatures from Fahrenheit to Centigrade. If you are not sure how the program works or what the variables do, try adding some PRINT lines to make the computer display the contents of the variables on the screen. This way you can look "inside" the program to help you understand how it works.

```
10  INPUT A
20  LET F=32
30  LET B=5
40  LET C=B/9
50  LET D=A-F
60  LET R=D*C
70  PRINT R
```

The Fahrenheit temperature you type in is stored in the variable A.

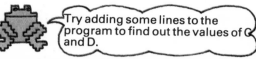

Try adding some lines to the program to find out the values of C and D.

Program puzzle
Now see if you can change this program to convert a temperature from Centigrade to Fahrenheit.

Program writing puzzles

In the boxes below there are some ideas for simple programs to write. You will need to use lots of variables so keep a note of them and the names you choose for them. It is a good idea to choose variable names that remind you of what the variables do, or what they stand for. Try writing the programs on paper first, then type them into a computer and debug them if necessary.

1 Do you speak Uglian?

You have been asked to go on a special mission to the Uglies who speak English but with the letters UG stuck onto the beginning of each word. Try writing a program to translate English words into Uglian.

Hints: Use LET with a string variable to hold the letters UG, and INPUT to ask for the English word. Then print out both the variables to display the Uglian word. Use PRINT statements to make the program clearer.

UGTAKE UGME UGTO UGYOUR UGLEADER

UGTHIS UGWAY

2 Speed calculator

Can you write a program to calculate speed? You will need INPUT lines for the time and distance, a sum to calculate the speed and PRINT lines to make the program clear.

3 Sausage program

Robot 1 eats 30 sausages an hour but Robot 2 can only eat 20 in the same time. If Robot 2 wants to eat at least 35 sausages and Robot 1 refuses to eat slower, how many sausages must they buy and how long will they take to eat them all?

Hints: Start with three variables, two to hold the numbers of sausages the robots can eat and one to hold the number Robot 2 wants to eat. Use more variables to hold the time Robot 2 takes to eat 35 sausages and the number of sausages Robot 1 can eat in that time.

Repeating things

It is very useful to be able to make the computer repeat something several times. One way to do this is with a loop using the words FOR, TO and NEXT. Try running the program on the right to see how a loop works.

J is a variable which acts as a counter. It tells the computer how many times to repeat line 20.

This line tells the computer to go back to the beginning of the loop.

```
10 FOR J=1 TO 10
20 PRINT "HELLO"
30 NEXT J
```

```
10 FOR K=1 TO 10
20 PRINT K
30 NEXT K
```

```
10 FOR I=1 TO 10
20 PRINT I;" X 8 ";
30 PRINT "= ";I*8
40 NEXT I
```

```
10 FOR L=1 TO 15
20 PRINT TAB(L);
   "HELLO"
30 NEXT L
```

The letters I, J, K and L are usually used as variable names in loops.

You can see how the loop variable works by putting in a PRINT command to display its value. You can also use the value of the variable inside the loop. Try these.

Loop puzzles

1
```
HELLO HELLO HELLO H
ELLO HELLO HELLO HE
LLO HELLO HELLO HEL
LO HELLO HELLO HELL
```

2
```
      HELLO
      HELLO
      HELLO
      HELLO
      HELLO
      HELLO
```

3
```
10 FOR I=1 TO 20
20 LET I=I-1
30 PRINT I
40 NEXT I
```

Can you write a simple loop program to fill your screen with HELLOs, and another to print a column of HELLOs down the centre of the screen?

What's wrong with the program above? Try it and see.

Steps

```
10 FOR I=1 TO 25 STEP 5
20 PRINT I
30 NEXT I
```

```
10 FOR J=20 TO 1 STEP-1
20 PRINT J
30 NEXT J
```

You can change the way that the variable counts by using the word STEP and a number which tells the computer to count in steps of that number. If you use a negative number the computer will count backwards. Run these programs, they try changing the STEP numbers.

1
```
      HELLO
      HELLO
      HELLO
      HELLO
      HELLO
      HELLO
```
Use TAB.

2
```
5    25
4    16
3     9
2     4
1     1
0     0
```

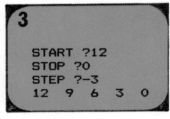

3
```
START ?12
STOP ?0
STEP ?-3
12  9  6  3  0
```

Can you write the programs to make your screen look like these?

Delay loops

Computers work at different speeds so you might need to make the loop bigger or smaller by changing the figure 1000.

```
10 FOR J=10 TO 1 STEP-1
20 PRINT J
30 NEXT J
40 FOR K=1 TO 1000
50 NEXT K
60 PRINT "LIFT OFF"
```

```
SECRET MESSAGE
MEMORISE IN 5 SECONDS
THEN IT WILL DISAPPEAR

MEET AGENT X.   2.00   AIRPORT
```

A delay loop is an empty loop with no instructions in it. In this program lines 40-50 make the computer count from 1 to 1000 and this makes it pause a moment.

Try writing the program to make your computer print out a secret message like the one above, then make it disappear after 5 seconds. To do this you need a delay loop followed by your computer's command to clear the screen. Experiment to find the correct figure to put in the delay loop.

Pattern puzzles

1
```
10 LET A$="***"
20 FOR J=1 TO 7
30 PRINT TAB(J);A$
40 NEXT J
50 FOR K=1 TO 3
60 PRINT TAB(J+1);A$
70 NEXT K
80 FOR L=7 TO 1 STEP-1
90 PRINT TAB(L);A$
100 NEXT L
```

You can use graphics characters instead of stars if your computer has them.

```
80 FOR L=8 TO 18
90 PRINT TAB(L);A$;"**"
100 NEXT L
```

The program on the left makes a pattern of stars on the screen. Try running it then change it to make different patterns. One idea is given above.

2
```
10 CLS
20 LET A=15
30 PRINT TAB(A);"*"
40 FOR K=1 TO .9
*50 PRINT TAB( ? );"*";
*60 PRINT TAB( ? );"*"
*70 ?
```

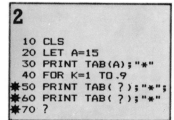

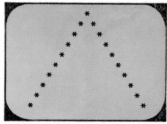

Can you complete lines 50 to 70 of this program so that your screen looks like the one above?

Now change the program to print the shape upside down.

4
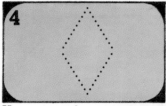

You can put the programs from puzzles 2 and 3 together to make a diamond shape.

5
Try printing the patterns in different colours.*

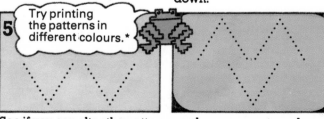

See if you can alter the pattern puzzle programs to make patterns like these.

*Look up the colour commands for your computer in your manual.

9

Loop puzzles

You can use loops inside other loops. These are known at nested loops. Each time the outside loop is repeated, the nested loop will run a certain number of times.

```
10 FOR K=1 TO 3
20 FOR L=1 TO 5 ─┐
30 PRINT K,L      ├── Nested loop
40 NEXT L        ─┘
50 NEXT K
```

This program prints out the values of the loop variables so you can see how the nested loop works.

```
10 FOR I=1 TO 4
20 FOR J=1 TO 4
30 PRINT
40 NEXT J
50 PRINT "HELLO"
60 NEXT I
```

Run this program then try changing the size of the loops. Can you add another nested loop to make the program run more slowly?

Bugs in loops

```
10 FOR L=1 TO 15
20 PRINT TAB(5);"*";
TAB(10);"*"
30 FOR J=1 TO 5
40 PRINT
50 NEXT J
60 NEXT L
```

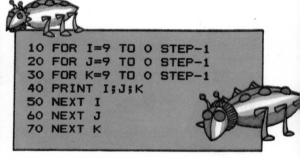

```
10 FOR I=9 TO O STEP-1
20 FOR J=9 TO O STEP-1
30 FOR K=9 TO O STEP-1
40 PRINT I;J;K
50 NEXT I
60 NEXT J
70 NEXT K
```

You must be careful to put both parts of the nested loop inside the other one or you will get a bug. The program on the left is correct but you must spot the mistakes in the program on the right and correct them.

Binary counter

```
10 FOR A=0 TO 1
20 FOR B=0 TO 1
30 FOR C=0 TO 1
40 FOR D=0 TO 1
50 PRINT D+C*2+B*4+A*8; " = ";
60 PRINT A;B;C;D
70 NEXT D
80 NEXT C
90 NEXT B
100 NEXT A
```

Line 50 works out the decimal value of each binary digit.

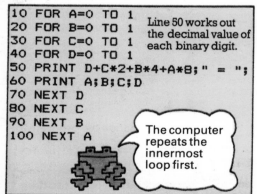

The computer repeats the innermost loop first.

This program uses four nested loops to count in binary. It can't count very far because it only uses four-figure binary numbers. Can you add more loops and change the PRINT lines to make a program that counts in eight-figure binary numbers?

Flashing message

DANGER
SPACE ATTACK

Can you write a program to print a message like this which flashes on and off? You will need a loop to clear the screen and print the message a number of times, and two delay loops so the message does not flash too fast.

Computer clock

Use a real clock to set the size of the delay loop to one second.

0:30

Try writing a program to make your computer run like a clock. You will need a loop for the seconds, one for the minutes, and a delay loop.

Rocket lift off program

Can you write a program using several loops to make a simple rocket shape "lift off" by moving slowly up the screen?

1. You will need to clear the screen then print lots of empty lines so your rocket is printed at the bottom of the screen.

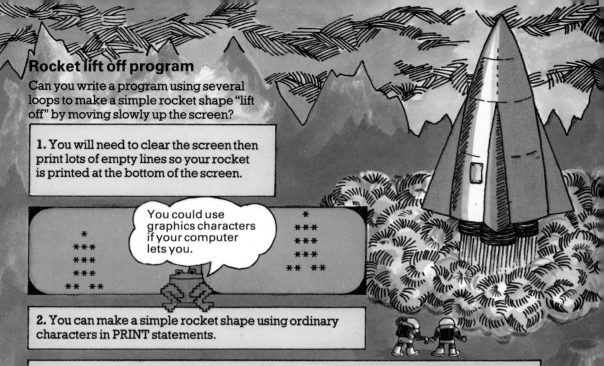

You could use graphics characters if your computer lets you.

```
    *
   ***
   ***
   ***
  ** **
```

```
    *
   ***
   ***
   ***
  ** **
```

2. You can make a simple rocket shape using ordinary characters in PRINT statements.

3. To make the rocket move up the screen, add more empty PRINT lines and a nested delay loop so the rocket does not move too fast.

Jumping man program

See if you can write a simple animation program to make a figure like the one on the right, jump up and down as it moves across the screen.

```
<O>        O      <O>        O      <O>        O
 O        <O>      O        <O>      O        <O>
/ \       / \     / \       / \     / \       / \
```

Drawing the figures

You can draw a simple figure in two different positions like those on the right, using PRINT with letters and symbols.

```
PRINT "<O>"
PRINT " O "
PRINT "/ \"
```

Add your own line numbers.

You need this empty line to make the figure appear to jump.

```
PRINT
PRINT " O "
PRINT "<O>"
PRINT "/ \"
```

Writing the program

1. You will need a loop the size of the width of your screen. It should count in steps of 2. You will see why when you come to writing the PRINT TAB instructions.

2. Inside the loop you have to clear the screen then PRINT the first figure. Use TAB so the position of the figure changes each time it is printed.

3. Add a delay loop so the figure stays on the screen for a moment.

4. Repeat this routine with a different TAB instruction for the second figure.

```
<O>    O   <O>    O   <O>    O   <O>    O   <O>    O   <O>    O   <O>
 O   <O>    O   <O>    O   <O>    O   <O>    O   <O>    O   <O>    O
/ \   / \  / \   / \  / \   / \  / \   / \  / \   / \  / \   / \  / \
```

IF/THEN exercises

You use the words IF and THEN to compare pieces of information and tell the computer to do different things according to the results.

```
10 LET A=8
20 INPUT B
30 IF B=A THEN PRINT "THEY'RE EQUAL"
40 IF B<>A THEN PRINT "THEY AREN'T
EQUAL"
50 IF B<A THEN PRINT B;" IS LESS
THAN ";A
60 IF B>A THEN PRINT B;" IS MORE
THAN ";A
```

Try running this program to make sure you know the meaning of the symbols that the computer uses to compare pieces of information.

```
10 PRINT "HOW MANY CHIPS CAN YOU
EAT?"
20 INPUT C
30 IF C>=0 AND C<=10 THEN
PRINT "YOU'LL STARVE"
40 IF C>10 AND C<=25 THEN
PRINT "NOT MANY"
50 IF C>25 AND C<=1000 THEN
PRINT "GREEDY"
60 IF C<0 OR C>1000 THEN PRINT "!!!"
```

Most computers let you compare several things at once using the words AND and OR in IF/THEN statements. Try running this program to see how they work.

Tables tester

```
10 LET A=13
20 FOR J=1 TO 13
30 PRINT "WHAT IS ";J;" X ";A;" ";
40 INPUT B
50 IF B=J*A THEN PRINT "CORRECT"
60 NEXT J
```

This is a program to test your 13 times table. Can you add more IF/THEN instructions to tell you when the answer is wrong and what it should be?

Password

```
10 LET S$="SAUSAGES"
20 PRINT "PASSWORD PLEASE ";
30 INPUT P$
40 IF P$=S$ THEN PRINT "O.K. CONTINUE"
```

Can you complete this program so the computer prints a message if you give the wrong password? Try adding to the program to make the computer ask for a secret number too.

Branching

You can give the computer lots of different instructions after the word THEN. For instance, you can tell the computer to stop the program or jump to another line using GOTO.

```
10 LET C=0
20 PRINT "ARE YOU BORED YET?"
30 INPUT B$
40 LET C=C+1
50 IF B$="YES" THEN STOP
60 IF C>10 THEN PRINT "YOU MUST BE"
70 IF B$="NO" THEN GOTO 20
80 PRINT "DON'T BE SILLY"
90 GOTO 20
```

What happens if you type "Bananas"?

In this program, the computer does different things depending on the answer you input at line 30. Run the program a few times using different answers.

Computer calculator

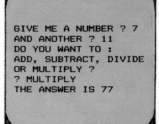

```
GIVE ME A NUMBER ? 7
AND ANOTHER ? 11
DO YOU WANT TO :
ADD, SUBTRACT, DIVIDE
OR MULTIPLY ?
? MULTIPLY
THE ANSWER IS 77
```

Here is the output from a program which can add, subtract, divide or multiply the two numbers which you type in. See if you can write the program for it, then try changing it to carry out different calculations.

Guessing games

Add some lines to the program for a clue to help you guess the word.

```
1
10  INPUT X
20  CLS
30  PRINT "GUESS
NUMBER"
40  INPUT Y
50  IF Y=X THEN GOTO
70
60  GOTO 30
70  PRINT "CORRECT"
```

1. Make the computer tell you when your guess is too small or too big, to help you guess correctly.

2. Add a variable to count how many guesses you make, then set a limit to the number of guesses allowed using IF/THEN.

```
2
CLUE
CROAKING CREATURE
? TOAD
NO
? FROG
YES
```

This is a program for a simple number guessing game. One person chooses a number, the other has to try and guess it. See if you can improve the program following the suggestions listed above.

Here is a screen showing a word guessing game. Can you write the program? It is similar to the number game except it uses strings.

Horse race

Here is a listing for a horse race game . . . but it is incomplete. See if you can fill in the missing line numbers after GOTO in the lines marked with an asterisk. You can find out how to play the game and ways to improve it below.

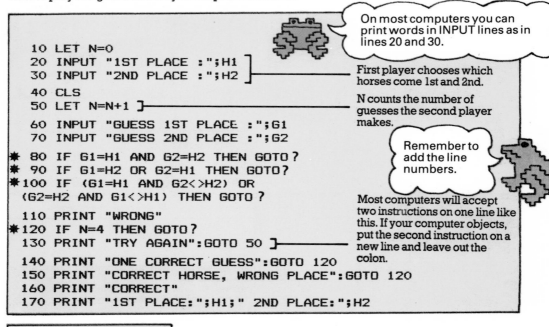

On most computers you can print words in INPUT lines as in lines 20 and 30.

```
    10  LET N=0
    20  INPUT "1ST PLACE :";H1
    30  INPUT "2ND PLACE :";H2
    40  CLS
    50  LET N=N+1
    60  INPUT "GUESS 1ST PLACE :";G1
    70  INPUT "GUESS 2ND PLACE :";G2
*   80  IF G1=H1 AND G2=H2 THEN GOTO ?
*   90  IF G1=H2 OR G2=H1 THEN GOTO ?
* 100  IF (G1=H1 AND G2<>H2) OR
    (G2=H2 AND G1<>H1) THEN GOTO ?
   110  PRINT "WRONG"
* 120  IF N=4 THEN GOTO ?
   130  PRINT "TRY AGAIN":GOTO 50
   140  PRINT "ONE CORRECT GUESS":GOTO 120
   150  PRINT "CORRECT HORSE, WRONG PLACE":GOTO 120
   160  PRINT "CORRECT"
   170  PRINT "1ST PLACE:";H1;" 2ND PLACE:";H2
```

First player chooses which horses come 1st and 2nd.

N counts the number of guesses the second player makes.

Remember to add the line numbers.

Most computers will accept two instructions on one line like this. If your computer objects, put the second instruction on a new line and leave out the colon.

How to play

There are six horses numbered 1 to 6. The first player chooses which horses come 1st and 2nd. The second player has four goes to guess which they are.

Ideas to improve the game

1. Invent a scoring system and write it into the program.

2. Give the players the choice of running again.

Random numbers

The word RND produces a random number, but the way the command is used varies from computer to computer. The different instructions are given below, but you should check the correct command for your computer in your manual or the conversion chart at the back of the book. Then see if you can do the exercises and puzzles on these two pages.

```
PRINT RND(99)
PRINT RND(10)
```

```
PRINT INT(RND(1)*99+1)
PRINT INT(RND(0)*99+1)
PRINT INT(RND*99+1)
```

Check whether your computer needs (1) or (0) after RND.

On some computers you just use RND with a number in brackets to produce a whole number between one and the number in brackets.

To get a whole random number on most computers you need to use the word INT with RND followed by (1) or (0) if necessary. Then you multiply by the number of figures in the range you want and add the first number. For instance, all the commands in the box above tell the computer to pick a random number between 1 and 99.

```
PRINT RND(6)+5
PRINT INT(RND(1)*6+5)
PRINT INT(RND(0)*6+5)
PRINT INT(RND*6+5)
```

These instructions produce a random number between 5 and 10. Try out the right one for your computer.

Can you work out how to make your computer produce random numbers between 10 and 20?

`INT(RND(1)*10+1)`

In this book the RND instructions are written like this. Remember to convert them if necessary.

Program puzzle

Look back at the number guessing game on page 13 and see if you can alter it so that the computer selects a random number between 1 and 20 for you to guess.

Number sequence

```
GUESS THE NEXT
NUMBER IN THIS
SEQUENCE
   4   13   22
? 31
CORRECT
```

```
*10 LET X= ?
*20 LET Y= ?
 30 FOR I=1 TO 3
 40 PRINT X+I*Y
 50 NEXT I
```

```
PRINT X+I*I
PRINT I*I-Y
PRINT X+Y-I*I
PRINT Y+X^I
```

See if you can write the program for this number sequence game shown on the screen above. Part of the program is given above (centre).

You will have to fill in the random number commands in lines 10 and 20 and add some PRINT and IF/THEN lines. On the right there are some ideas for changing line 40 to make different number sequences. Can you think of a way to extend the program so that the computer picks a sequence at random each time you run the program?

Escape from Zorgos

See if you can write the program for this game. You are stranded on the alien planet Zorgos and you need 50 Zchips to fuel your planet-mobile with enough memory to find its way back to Earth. You have been given 10 Zchips but the only way to get any more is to win them by playing a risky game of chance with an alien computer. The screens below show you a sample run of the game.

```
YOU HAVE 10 CHIPS
PLACE YOUR BET : 5
PRESS P TO THROW:P
       5    2
KEEP YOUR BET
```

```
YOU HAVE 10 CHIPS
PLACE YOUR BET : 9
PRESS P TO THROW:P
       6    4
YOU TRIPLED YOUR BET
YOU HAVE 28 CHIPS
```

DICE	YOUR BET
DOUBLES:	DOUBLED
10 OR 11:	TRIPLED
6 OR 7:	KEEP YOUR BET
OTHERS:	LOST

You place a bet of Zchips and depending on what numbers come up when the computer throws two dice, you will win, lose or keep your bet. If you get doubles your bet is doubled, if the numbers add up to 10 or 11, your bet is tripled and so on as shown in the chart on the right.

Paper, Stone or Scissors: Spot the bugs

This is a program for the game Paper, Stone or Scissors to play against the computer, but it is full of bugs. Using the notes on the right which tell you how the program is supposed to work, see if you can spot the mistakes and correct them so that the program runs properly.

```
 10 CLS
 20 LET C=0
 30 LET A=0
 40 LET F=0
 50 LET R=INT(RND(1)*4+1)
 60 IF R=1 THEN LET C$="PAPER"
 70 IF R=2 THEN LET C$="STONE"
 80 IF R=3 C$="SCISSORS"
 90 PRINT "I'M READY"
100 PRINT "DO YOU WANT PAPER, STONE, OR SCISSORS"
110 INPUT A$
120 PRINT
130 IF C$="PAPER" AND A$="SCISSORS" THEN LET F=1
140 IF C$="STONE" AND A$="PAPER" THEN LET F=1
150 IF A$="SCISSORS" AND A$="STONE" THEN LET F=1
160 IF C$=A$ THEN LET F=2
170 PRINT "YOU CHOSE ";A$
180 PRINT "I CHOSE ";C$
190 PRINT "SO"
200 IF F=0 THEN PRINT "I WIN"
210 IF F=F THEN PRINT "YOU WIN"
220 IF F=2 THEN PRINT "IT'S A DRAW"
230 IF F=0 THEN LET A=A+1
240 IF F=1 THEN LET C=C+1
250 PRINT "THE SCORE IS:"
260 PRINT "ME  : ";C
270 PRINT "YOU : ";A
280 IF C>10 AND A>10 THEN GOTO 40
290 PRINT "THAT IS THE END"
```

C keeps count of the computer's score.
A keeps count of your score.
F tells the computer who has won in lines 130-160.

The computer's choice of paper, stone or scissors is stored in C$ and depends on the value of R.

The IF . . . THEN lines work out who wins. If you win, the computer makes F equal 1 and if it is a draw then F is 2. Otherwise, F stays at 0 which means that the computer wins.

The computer tells you who is the winner and works out the score by testing the value of F.

Do you remember how this game works? Paper covers stone, stone blunts scissors and scissors cut paper.

Character crunching

The computer can do all sorts of things with the characters inside strings. The programs on this page show some of the commands that BASIC uses for handling strings and how they work. If you have a Sinclair (Timex) computer, you will have to use some different instructions as shown below.

```
LET R$="ROBOT"
PRINT LEFT$(R$,3)
PRINT RIGHT$(R$,3)

LET C$="CHIPMUNK"
PRINT LEFT$(C$,4)
PRINT RIGHT$(C$,7)
```

LEFT$ and RIGHT$ tell the computer to take a number of characters from the left or right hand side of the string. You tell the computer how many characters to take by putting the number in brackets.

```
10 LET K$="KANGAROO"
20 PRINT "POSITION OF"
30 PRINT "FIRST LETTER";
40 INPUT S
50 PRINT "HOW MANY LETTERS";
60 INPUT N
70 PRINT MID$(K$,S,N)
```

MID$ tells the computer to take the middle letters of a string. The first number inside the brackets tells the computer where to start counting and the second tells it how many letters to take.

> The computer counts spaces in the same way as letters and symbols.

```
10 PRINT "WORD PLEASE"
20 INPUT W$
30 LET L=LEN(W$)
40 PRINT "THERE ARE ";
50 PRINT L;" LETTERS";
60 PRINT " IN THE WORD ";W$
```

The word LEN counts the number of characters in a string. Try this program to see how it works.

Sinclair (Timex) computers

```
LET A$="ABCDEFGHIJKLMNOP"
PRINT A$(4 TO 6)
DEF
PRINT A$(14 TO 16)
NOP
```

Sinclair (Timex) computers do not use LEFT$, RIGHT$ or MID$. Instead you tell the computer which characters to select in the way shown above.

String puzzles

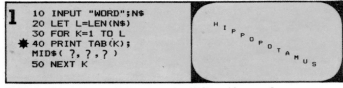

1
```
10 INPUT "WORD";N$
20 LET L=LEN(N$)
30 FOR K=1 TO L
✱ 40 PRINT TAB(K);
   MID$( ?,?,? )
50 NEXT K
```

Can you fill in the question marks in line 40 to make your screen look like this? Hint: you can use MID$ to pick out one character from a string at a time.

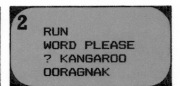

2
```
RUN
WORD PLEASE
? KANGAROO
OORAGNAK
```

Try making the computer print a word backwards using MID$ and a step -1 loop.

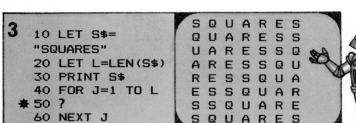

3
```
10 LET S$=
   "SQUARES"
20 LET L=LEN(S$)
30 PRINT S$
40 FOR J=1 TO L
✱ 50 ?
60 NEXT J
```

```
S Q U A R E S
Q U A R E S S
U A R E S S Q
A R E S S Q U
R E S S Q U A
E S S Q U A R
S S Q U A R E
S Q U A R E S
```

> Using LEFT$ and RIGHT$, see if you can fill in the missing line in this program to make this appear on the screen.

16

Longest word

At line 50 you need to tell the computer to store the longest word entered so far in variable A$. Try using IF/THEN and LEN.

```
10  LET A$=""
20  PRINT "WORDS PLEASE"
30  FOR J=1 TO 5
40  INPUT W$
*50  ?
60  NEXT J
70  PRINT "LONGEST WORD :"
80  PRINT A$
```

```
WORDS PLEASE
? CAT
? LIZARD
? HIPPOPOTAMUS
? COBRA
? ANT
LONGEST WORD :
HIPPOPOTAMUS
```

This program finds the longest word out of a list of five. Fill in the missing line and try running it.

Shortest word

Can you write a program to find the shortest word? It is like the one above except that you need a variable which is longer than any of the words you type in for the computer to measure them against. You will need to change the IF/THEN instruction.

You can fill the variable with any characters, like this.

```
LET A$="XXX!!!&&ABC*
**123!!!!XXXXXXXXX"
```

Word editor

The listing below is for a word editing program which enables you to type in a sentence and then change the words in it. Before you can run the program, you must fill the gaps in the lines which are marked with an asterisk. Use the notes on the right of the program to help you.

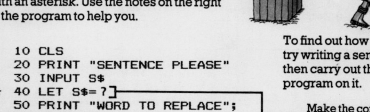

```
    10  CLS
    20  PRINT "SENTENCE PLEASE"
    30  INPUT S$
*   40  LET S$= ?
    50  PRINT "WORD TO REPLACE";
    60  INPUT W$
*   70  LET W$= ?
    80  PRINT "NEW WORD";
    90  INPUT N$
*  100  LET LS= ?
*  110  LET LW= ?
   120  LET A$=""
   130  LET K=1
*  140  IF MID$(S$, ? , ? )=W$ THEN
       LET A$=S$
*  150  IF A$=S$ THEN LET S$=LEFT$
       ( ? , ? ) + ? +RIGHT$(A$,LS-(K+LW-2) )
   160  LET LS=LEN(S$)
   170  LET K=K+1
*  180  IF K<=LS-LW+1 THEN GOTO ?
   190  PRINT S$
   200  GOTO 50
```

To find out how this program works, try writing a sentence on paper and then carry out the instructions in the program on it.

Make the computer add a space to the beginning and end of S$ and W$. Do you know why?

Make LS equal the length of the sentence (S$) and LW the length of the word (W$).

Complete this line to make the computer search for the word to replace (W$) in the sentence. Hint: use K to count the characters.

This line makes the computer work out the number of characters to the left of the word you want to remove, then insert the new word and add the rest of the sentence. Can you fill in the missing variables and figure?

More character crunching

Inside the computer, characters are represented by number codes and you can do things with characters by using these code numbers. The word CHR$ converts a number into a character. ASC (or CODE on Sinclair (Timex) computers) does the opposite and converts a character into its code number. Most home computers use a standard code for the numbers, called ASCII* code, although the ZX81 (Timex 1000) has its own. You will find a code chart for your computer in your manual.

Using CHR$

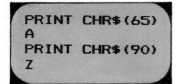

```
PRINT CHR$(65)
A
PRINT CHR$(90)
Z
```

If you have a ZX81 (Timex 1000), you should use these numbers.

```
PRINT CHR$(38)
A
PRINT CHR$(63)
Z
```

Try some PRINT CHR$ commands using these and other numbers. Some numbers are set aside for keys such as SPACE and RETURN so nothing will appear on the screen. You can find out which these are from your manual.

Letter puzzles

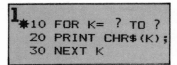

```
1. *10 FOR K= ? TO ?
   20 PRINT CHR$(K);
   30 NEXT K
```

See if you can insert the correct numbers in the loop to make the program print out the alphabet.

```
2. abcdefghijklm
   nopqrstuvwxyz
```

Try writing a loop to print the alphabet in small (lower case) letters if your computer uses them.

```
3. I D I P Q C H K A
   S K Q C H U A M S
   S N M Q T O P X A
```

Can you write a short program to produce a series of random letters on the screen?

Using ASC or CODE

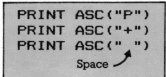

```
PRINT ASC("P")
PRINT ASC("+")
PRINT ASC(" ")
```
Space

```
PRINT CODE("4")
PRINT CODE("U")
PRINT CODE("C")
```

What happens if you put lots of characters in the brackets after ASC or CODE?

Try using ASC (or CODE on Sinclair (Timex) computers) with these and other characters to see what numbers your computer produces.

Comparing letters

```
?P,O
O COMES BEFORE P
?L,B
B COMES BEFORE L
?S,C
C COMES BEFORE S
```

Using the symbols > and < try writing a program which makes the computer compare any two letters then puts them in alphabetical order.

Capital converter

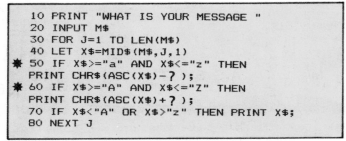

```
10 PRINT "WHAT IS YOUR MESSAGE "
20 INPUT M$
30 FOR J=1 TO LEN(M$)
40 LET X$=MID$(M$,J,1)
* 50 IF X$>="a" AND X$<="z" THEN
   PRINT CHR$(ASC(X$)-? );
* 60 IF X$>="A" AND X$<="Z" THEN
   PRINT CHR$(ASC(X$)+? );
70 IF X$<"A" OR X$>"z" THEN PRINT X$;
80 NEXT J
```

See if you can fill in the missing numbers in lines 50 and 60 to make the computer convert a message from small letters to capitals or from capitals to small letters. You will not be able to run this program if your computer only uses capital letters.

18

*ASCII stands for American Standard Code for Information Interchange.

Code writing programs

Here are some ideas for programs to convert messages into secret code. The chart on the right shows how the first program works. Fill in the missing numbers and symbols in the program, then try running it.

Secret code writer

The letters are shifted alternately forwards and backwards by one letter in the alphabet.

Can you put the last word into code?

```
-+-+-+-+-+-+-+-+-+-+-+
THE PLANE LEAVES TONIGHT
SID OMZOD KFZWDT UN
```

Secret code writer program

```
    10 PRINT "WHAT IS YOUR MESSAGE"
    20 INPUT M$
*   30 FOR J=1 TO?
*   40 LET X=?
*   50 IF X<? OR X>? THEN LET N=X:
       GOTO 100
*   60 IF INT(J/2)=J/2 THEN LET N=X?1
*   70 IF INT(J/2)<>J/2 THEN LET N=X?1
*   80 IF N<? THEN LET N=N+26
*   90 IF N>? THEN LET N=N-26
*  100 PRINT?
   110 NEXT J
```

Make the loop the same size as the number of characters in M$.

Make the computer select one letter at a time and store its ASCII code number in X.*

Insert two numbers to check each character and make sure it is a letter. (Numbers and spaces stay the same in this secret code.)

To shift the letters, add 1 to X if the loop counter (J) is an even number and subtract 1 if it is odd.

100 PRINT? — Print the coded letter using CHR$.

If the shifted number (N) runs off either end of the alphabet, send it back to the other end by adding or subtracting 26.

Key number code	◄— N=X+Key number —► N=N-26
Alphabet	A B C D E F G H I J K L M N O P Q R S T U V W X Y Z
Code alphabet	G H I J K L M N O P Q R S T U V W X Y Z A B C D E F

In this code the alphabet is shifted along a certain number (N) of letters. How far it shifts depends on a key number. In this example the key number is 6 so the alphabet is shifted along six letters. See if you can write the program, following the steps in the program above. You can use whatever key number you like.

Loopy code

```
J=1 2 3 4 5 6 7 8 9 10 11 12
  M E E T   A G E N T     X
```

In this code you add the value of the loop counter variable (J) to the ASCII number for each letter. See if you can write two programs, one to code a message and the other to work as a decoder.

Reverse code

```
CONTACT SECRET AGENT
OCT NCA TESR CTEA EG TN
```

For this code you divide the message up into pairs of letters and swap the position of each letter in the pair including the spaces. To write the program, use a step 2 loop and print each pair of letters in reverse order.

*If you have a ZX81 (Timex 1000), use the computer's own code numbers.

HTSII S AESRCTEM SEASEGI NEREVSR EOCED

INKEY$ exercises

The word INKEY$ makes the computer look at the keyboard and see if a key has been pressed, but unlike INPUT, the computer will not stop and wait for you. The program will carry on running instead. Some computers use a different word for INKEY$, so first check your computer's command and then try the exercises on this page.

You don't need to press RETURN with these commands.

INKEY$
KEY$
GET
INKEY$(0)

```
10 LET A$=INKEY$
20 IF A$="" THEN PRINT "!";
30 IF A$<>"" THEN PRINT A$;
40 GOTO 10
```

Try running this program using the correct command for your computer. When you press a key the computer prints that character, otherwise it prints an exclamation mark.

These are some of the words used for INKEY$ on different computers. Check your manual or the conversion chart on page 47 for the command your computer understands.

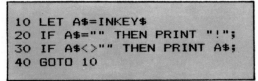

```
HELLO          HELLO          H
ELLO     HELLO          HELL
O              HELLO     HELLO
HELLO          HELLO     HEL
LO       HELLO          HELLO
```

Now see if you can write a program to make your computer print the word HELLO when you press a key, and otherwise print a space as shown on the screen above. The program is similar to the one on the left.

Making the computer wait

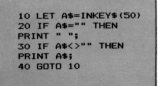

```
10 LET A$=INKEY$(50)
20 IF A$="" THEN
PRINT " ";
30 IF A$<>"" THEN
PRINT A$;
40 GOTO 10
```

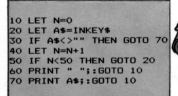

```
10 LET N=0
20 LET A$=INKEY$
30 IF A$<>"" THEN GOTO 70
40 LET N=N+1
50 IF N<50 THEN GOTO 20
60 PRINT " ";:GOTO 10
70 PRINT A$;:GOTO 10
```

Can you think of a way to make the computer wait indefinitely until a key is pressed?

It is sometimes useful to make the computer wait a little before continuing with the program. In some versions of BASIC you have to put a number in brackets after INKEY$ as shown above left. This tells the computer how long to wait (in fractions of a second) before continuing. If your computer does not let you do this, you can still make it wait by putting INKEY$ inside a loop using GOTO as shown above right.

High speed maths bugs

Can you spot the bugs in this program and correct them to make the program run properly? The computer should select two numbers between 1 and 25 at random. You must add them together and press any key as soon as the right answer appears on the screen.

```
10 CLS
20 PRINT "PRESS ANY KEY WHEN YOU
30 PRINT "SEE THE RIGHT ANSWER TO
THE SUM"
40 LET N=0
50 LET X=INT(RND(1)+25+1)
60 LET Y=INT(RND(1)*25+1)
70 PRINT
80 PRINT "X;" + ";Y;" = "
90 LET N=N+1
100 PRINT N
110 LET INKEY$=A$
```

```
120 IF A$<>"" THEN GOTO 180
130 FOR K=1 TO 100:NEXT K
140 IF N<30 THEN GOTO 90
150 PRINT "BAD LUCK. ANSWER IS ";X+Y
160 FOR K=1 TO 1000:NEXT T
170 GOTO 30
180 IF N<>X+Y THEN GOTO 150
190 PRINT "YES. THE ANSWER IS X+Y"
```

There are eight bugs in this program.

How to write a car crash game

Following the steps below, see if you can write the program for this car crash game. The screen on the right shows what the game should look like. To display the car and the road on the screen, you can use PRINT TAB with a * for the car and ! for each side of the road. The road zig-zags down the screen while you steer the car with two keys to stop it crashing into the road.

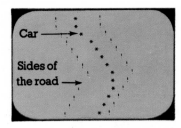

Car →

Sides of the road →

1. Setting up the variables

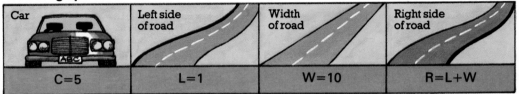

Car	Left side of road	Width of road	Right side of road
C=5	L=1	W=10	R=L+W

You need four variables C, L, W and R to work out the TAB positions for the car and sides of the road. You might need to change the numbers given above to fit your screen. Clear the screen and set up these variables in the first five lines.

2. Drawing the road

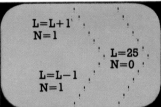

L=L+1
N=1

L=25
N=0

L=L-1
N=1

> You must include the line LET R=L+W in the repeat to make sure the value of R changes with L.

Now make the computer display the road and car using PRINT TAB with a variable and symbol. Use GOTO to repeat the instructions and draw a long straight road.

To make the road zig-zag you must insert some lines to change the value of L each time the PRINT TAB instructions are repeated. You must also make sure the road does not go off the screen. To do this, you need another variable (N). Set this to 1 if L <= 1 and to 0 if L >= the width of your screen. Then tell the computer to add or subtract 1 from L depending on the value of N.

3. Steering the car

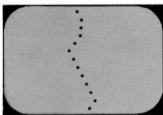

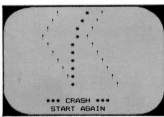

*** CRASH ***
START AGAIN

To steer the car you need an INKEY$ line. Then choose two keys (such as < and >) and add or subtract 1 from C depending on which key is pressed. If the program runs too fast for you to steer the car, add a delay loop.

Finally you must check to see if the car has crashed into the sides of the road by comparing C with L and R. If there is a crash you must tell the player and start again.

> Can you make the road zig-zag in a random pattern?

> Can you invent a scoring system?

21

DATA puzzles

One of the easiest ways of giving the computer large amounts of information is with the words READ and DATA. A DATA line contains a list of words or numbers and READ tells the computer to store the data in one or more variables. If you have a ZX81 (Timex 1000) you will not be able to run the programs on these two pages as your computer does not use these commands, but on page 24 there is an alternative method of storing DATA using an array.

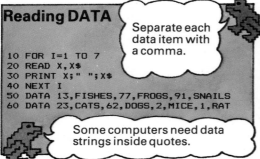

Reading DATA

Separate each data item with a comma.

```
10 FOR I=1 TO 7
20 READ X,X$
30 PRINT X;" ";X$
40 NEXT I
50 DATA 13,FISHES,77,FROGS,91,SNAILS
60 DATA 23,CATS,62,DOGS,2,MICE,1,RAT
```

Some computers need data strings inside quotes.

Run this program to see how READ and DATA work. The word READ is followed by two variables and each time the loop repeats the computer stores the next pair of data items in the variables X and X$.

Name check

Replace the question mark in line 50 with the last name in your data.

```
10 PRINT "NAME PLEASE ";
20 INPUT N$
30 READ X$
40 IF X$=N$ THEN GOTO 70
★ 50 IF X$=" ? " THEN PRINT "YOUR
   NAME ISN'T ON THE LIST":STOP
60 GOTO 30
70 PRINT "O.K. YOUR NAME IS ON
   THE LIST"
★ 80 DATA?
```

In this program the computer asks your name and checks it against a list of names stored as data. Try putting your own data in line 80 (you can add as many names as you like) then put the last name in line 50 to tell the computer to stop the program after reading the last name in the list.

Restoring DATA

```
★ 10 FOR J= ? TO ?}
★ 20 FOR I= ? TO ?}
  30 READ N$
★ 40 IF LEFT$(N$,1)=CHR$( ? ) THEN PRINT N$
  50 NEXT I
  60 RESTORE
  70 NEXT J
  80 DATA VERA,XAVIER,ZACHARY,HORACE,BIGGLES,BILL,BEN
  90 DATA TOPSY,TIM,POPEYE,JIM,HARRY,GEORGE,DELILAH
 100 DATA LOVEDAY,HONORA,SAMPSON,SAUL,TABITHA
```

Make the J loop the length of the alphabet using character code numbers.

Make the I loop the same size as the number of data items.

Can you complete this program to sort names into alphabetical order? The names are listed in DATA lines and RESTORE tells the computer to go back to the beginning of the data list each time the J loop is repeated. See if you can fill in the missing variables and numbers to run the program.

Spot the bug puzzles

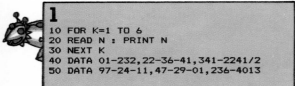

1
```
10 FOR K=1 TO 6
20 READ N : PRINT N
30 NEXT K
40 DATA 01-232,22-36-41,341-2241/2
50 DATA 97-24-11,47-29-01,236-4013
```

2
```
10 READ X
20 PRINT X
30 GOTO 10
40 DATA 1,461,892,66,1471,4462,1,3
50 DATA 53,80,241,90,371,825,33,13
```

In this program a list of telephone numbers is stored in the data lines. Can you spot the bugs in the program, and correct them?

If you cannot spot the bug in this program, try running it. The computer should print an error message to tell you what is wrong. Can you think of an easy way to solve this problem?

Joe's cafe

```
JOE'S CAFE
1.99   FRENCH SNAIL STEW
0.80   SAUSAGE SOUP
1.10   PIGEON PIE
0.99   MEAT BALL MASH
0.05   LETTUCE LEAF
0.60   ICE CREAM SODA
0.87   PEANUT BUTTER PIZZA
1.30   POPEYE'S SPINACH SPECIAL
0.40   BARBECUED BREAD
0.58   PEPPERMINT MILKSHAKE
```

```
WELCOME TO JOE'S CAFE
HOW MUCH CAN YOU SPEND
? 0.75

HERE'S WHAT YOU CAN EAT

LETTUCE LEAF
ICE CREAM SODA
BARBECUED BREAD
PEPPERMINT MILKSHAKE
```

On the left above is the menu from Joe's cafe. Using the prices and items on the menu as data, see if you can write a program which tells you what you can buy to eat for a certain amount of money, as shown in the screen on the right. You can also add some more items to the menu.

Telephone directory

Below there are instructions for writing a telephone directory program. The screens on the right show you a sample run. See if you can write the program.

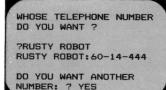

```
WHOSE TELEPHONE NUMBER
DO YOU WANT ?

?RUSTY ROBOT
RUSTY ROBOT:60-14-444

DO YOU WANT ANOTHER
NUMBER: ? YES
```

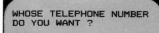

```
WHOSE TELEPHONE NUMBER
DO YOU WANT ?

?BERNIE THE BUG
NAME NOT LISTED

DO YOU WANT ANOTHER
NUMBER: ? NO
```

Store the numbers in a string variable. Do you know why?

Rusty Robot's number please.

1. Compile a list of your friends' names and telephone numbers in DATA statements as shown above.

2. Use PRINT to make the computer ask whose number you want, and INPUT for your answer.

3. Use READ to search for the name inside a loop. Use separate variables for the names and numbers.

```
RUSTY ROBOT
60-14-444
```
```
NAME NOT
LISTED
```

Do you want another number?   Yes!

START

4. Print the name and number (which should be the next item of data), or indicate that the name is not listed.

5. Make the computer ask if you want another number. Use INPUT for your answer.

6. Depending on the answer, RESTORE the data and go back to the beginning or stop the program.

Using arrays

A useful way of storing data is in an array. You can think of an array as a set of variables with each item of data stored in a numbered compartment. The data items are called elements. You can refer to an element by using the array name and its compartment number which is called a subscript.

Numeric arrays

Here is a numeric array called N. It contains six elements. You need to tell the computer how big an array will be so that it can put aside enough space in its memory. To do this you use the word DIM followed by the array name and the number of elements it contains. This is called dimensioning an array.

```
✸10 DIM ?
  20 FOR K=1 TO 6
  30 READ N(K)
  40 NEXT K
✸50 DATA ?
```

For ZX81 (Timex 1000)

```
✸ 10 DIM ?
  20 FOR K=1 TO 6
  30 INPUT N(K)
  40 NEXT K
```

```
N(1)  IS  1066
N(2)  IS  1216
N(3)  IS  1485
N(4)  IS  1603
N(5)  IS  1665
N(6)  IS  1959
```

```
1485    1216
1959    1485
1959    1665
1603    1603
1485    1216
```

To put data into an array you can use a loop with READ/DATA. See if you can complete the program on the left so it stores all the information in the picture above in an array. If you have a ZX81 (Timex 1000) try the program on the right which uses a series of INPUT statements to fill the array.

Now try writing a program to print the data stored in the array on the screen. Use PRINT and a loop variable as the subscript of the array. On the screen on the right, the computer prints elements of the array at random using a random number as the subscript of the array.

String arrays

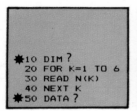

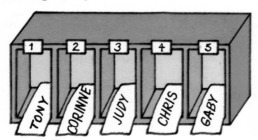

This is a string array (N$). It contains five names and so it has five elements. Unless you have a Sinclair (Timex) computer, you deal with string arrays in exactly the same way as numeric arrays. See if you can write a simple program to store the data in this array and then print the data on the screen.

Sinclair (Timex) computers

```
ARRAY A$
1   CAT
2   FISH
3   ELEPHANT
4   RAT
5   DONKEY
```

DIM A$(5,8)

Sinclair (Timex) computers hold each string in a separate row of an array and put each character of a string into a separate element. To dimension an array you must tell the computer how many strings (rows) there are and the number of characters (elements) in the longest string. Put both numbers in brackets as shown above. The computer makes all the rows the same length by adding spaces to the other strings.

Calendar calculator

✱ 10 ? ⎤———————— Dimension the arrays.
20 FOR K=1 TO 12

✱ 30 ? ⎤———————— READ the data into two arrays M$ and D.
40 NEXT K
50 PRINT "MONTH NUMBER ";
60 INPUT N

✱ 70 PRINT M$(?);" HAS "; ⎤ Fill in the missing subscripts to print the correct data from the arrays.
✱ 80 PRINT D(?);" DAYS" ⎦

✱ 90 DATA ? ⎤
✱ 100 DATA ? ⎥———— Put the name of each month followed by its number of days in data statements in these lines.
✱ 110 DATA ? ⎦

Can you complete this program so that when you type in the number of a month, the computer prints its name and the number of days it has? There are some hints alongside the program to help you.

```
WHAT IS THE NAME OF
THE MONTH ? JULY

JULY HAS 31 DAYS
```

Now alter the program so that the computer asks for the name of a month, then tells you the number of days in it. Use a loop and IF/THEN to search through M$ for the name of the month. Use the loop variable as the subscript to pick the right data item stored in D.

Make your mind up program

```
PICK A NUMBER FROM 1 TO 10
? 9
WHY DON'T YOU STAND ON YOUR HEAD
O.K. ? NO

PICK A NUMBER FROM 1 TO 10
? 5
WHY DON'T YOU FEED THE CAT
O.K. ? YES
```

Here is an idea for a program that could be very useful when you cannot decide what to do. To run the program you pick a number and the computer prints a suggestion on the screen.

To write the program you need a string array (I$) filled with ten ideas. INPUT a number into a variable (N) and make the computer pick one of the data items by using N as the subscript of I$.

Twenty questions

```
HOW MANY LEGS DOES A
CENTIPEDE HAVE ?
? 100
CORRECT

HOW MANY PLAYERS
IN A FOOTBALL TEAM ?
? 10
NO STUPID.
THE ANSWER IS 11.
```

This screen shows the output from a quiz game. To write the program, work out 20 questions and put them in a string array. Then put the answers in another array. The subscripts of the two arrays should link the questions with their answers.

Random number chart

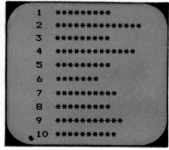

```
1  *********
2  *************
3  *********
4  *************
5  *********
6  *******
7  **********
8  *********
9  ***********
10 **********
```

```
10 LET N=0
20 DIM A(10)
30 FOR K=1 TO 10
40 LET A(K)=0
50 NEXT K
60 LET R=INT(RND(1)*10+1)
70 LET A(R)=A(R)+1
80 LET N=N+1
90 IF N<100 THEN GOTO 60
```

The computer gives each element of array A an initial value of 0.

This program uses an array to store the data for a chart. The computer picks 100 numbers from 1 to 10 at random. Each element of the array (A) keeps count of the number of times each number is picked. See if you can add to the program to make the computer print out a chart like the one above which prints one star for each number selected. To do this write a loop that repeats 10 times with another loop inside it. The nested loop should print one line of the chart at a time.

Writing subroutines

A subroutine is a section of a program for carrying out a particular task which is usually used several times during the program. The word GOSUB, followed by the number of the first line of the subroutine tells the computer to jump to the subroutine. The computer works through the subroutine until it meets the word RETURN. This sends it back to the main program starting at the instruction after the word GOSUB.

> Try running this program to see how the GOSUB/RETURN commands work.

```
  10 PRINT "HELLO ";
  20 GOSUB 1010
  30 PRINT "HELLO AGAIN ";
  40 GOSUB 1010
  50 PRINT "AND WHAT IS THIS ?"
  60 GOSUB 2020
  70 STOP
1010 PRINT "THIS IS A SUBROUTINE"
1020 RETURN
2020 PRINT "ANOTHER SUBROUTINE"
2030 RETURN
```

Ice cream survey			
MELON	16	MELON	****************
BANANA	11	BANANA	***********
GINGER	8	GINGER	********
GHERKIN	1	GHERKIN	*
BUBBLE GUM	18	BUBBLE GUM	******************

The table above left shows the results of a survey to find the most popular of six new ice cream flavours. Can you write a program to display this information as shown on the screen on the right? Use a loop to read the data into two arrays and, within the loop, send the computer to a subroutine to print one line of the chart at a time.

Sink the sub

The program below is for a game called "Sink the Sub". Hidden somewhere on an imaginary 10 × 10 grid is an alien submarine. The computer chooses its position by picking two random numbers which work as co-ordinates to pin-point its position on the grid. You have four chances to find the sub by guessing the co-ordinates X (across) and Y (up). If your guess is wrong, the computer jumps to a subroutine which tells you which direction to try next time. Before you can run the program, you must write the subroutine.

```
 10 CLS
 20 LET N=0
 30 LET X=INT(RND(1)*10+1)
 40 LET Y=INT(RND(1)*10+1)
 50 LET N=N+1

 60 PRINT "GUESS ";N;" ";
 70 INPUT A,B
 80 IF A=X AND B=Y THEN GOTO 170

 90 GOSUB 200
100 PRINT

110 IF N<=4 THEN GOTO 50
120 PRINT "YOU'VE RUN OUT OF GOES"

130 PRINT "DO YOU WANT TO PLAY AGAIN"

140 INPUT R$
150 IF LEFT$(R$,1)="Y" THEN GOTO 10

160 STOP

170 PRINT "YOU HIT THE SUB IN ";N;" GOES"

180 GOTO 130
```

> You could draw a grid like this to help you locate the submarine when you play the game.

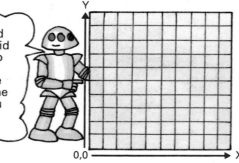

Writing the subroutine

You need several IF/THEN lines to compare your guess (A,B) with the sub's location (X,Y) and print a message on the screen. For instance, if B is less than Y, then you should try North, if A is less than X, then try East and so on.

Sample run

```
GUESS 1 ?3,2
YOU MISSED
TRY NORTH EAST
```

```
GUESS 2 ?3,3
YOU MISSED
TRY EAST
```

```
GUESS 3 ?5,3
YOU MISSED
TRY WEST
```

Fruit machine program to write

Can you write a program to make your computer work like a fruit machine? The screen on the right shows a sample run. You start with 10 tokens and it costs one token each time you play. Press any key to start and the computer prints the names of three "fruits" which are picked at random. Try following the instructions numbered below to help you write the program.

```
YOU HAVE 10 TOKENS
PRESS ANY KEY TO PLAY:P

BELL  BELL  LEMON

2 BELLS
YOU WIN 2 TOKENS
NOW YOU HAVE 11 TOKENS
PRESS ANY KEY TO PLAY:B
```

T is 10

1. First dimension an array F$ to hold the names of the six "fruits" shown above (lemon, cherries, plum, melon, grapes and bell). Store this data in F$ using READ/DATA (or INPUT).

2. Clear the screen and introduce a variable T to keep count out of the number of tokens. Give it an initial value of 10 and tell the player how many tokens there are.

3. Use INKEY$ to make the computer wait for the player to press any key to start. Subtract 1 from T (it costs one token to play) and clear the screen again.

R = 4

F$(R) is "BELL".

| 1 LEMON | 2 CHERRY | 3 MELON | 4 BELL | 5 GRAPE | 6 PLUM |

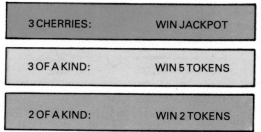

3 CHERRIES:	WIN JACKPOT
3 OF A KIND:	WIN 5 TOKENS
2 OF A KIND:	WIN 2 TOKENS

4. Make the computer pick a random number between one and six and store it in R. Use R as the subscript of F$ to select a fruit and store it in a variable A$. Repeat these instructions twice more to select two more fruits and store them in B$ and C$.

5. Next you must print the fruits on the screen and make the computer work out whether you have won anything or not. There are three ways to win as shown in the pictures above. For each type of win, send the computer to a different subroutine to print a suitable message and adjust the value of T.

T = 0

STOP

T = 1

START

6. Check to see that the player has at least one token left. If there are none (T= 0) then stop the program. Otherwise, send the computer back for another game.

7. If you use READ at the beginning of the program, remember to write the DATA lines. Add these to the end of the program.

How to write a treasure hunt program

On the next few pages there are step by step guidelines to writing a treasure hunt game in which you have to move through a maze of seven rooms collecting treasure. The program is fairly complicated so follow the directions carefully and test each stage as you go. If you get stuck on one part of the program you could look up the answer for that section, then continue with the rest of the program.

In order to write the program you need a good idea of how to play the game so read this section before you start.

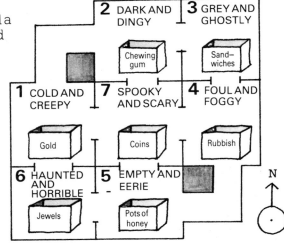

How to play

The map on the right shows the maze of seven rooms. Each has a different description and contains a box full of treasure. The information shown on this map is stored in the computer's memory but the map is not shown on the screen. This means that you have to work out the location of each room on this map as you play the game. Starting in a room selected at random, the object of the game is to get all the treasure into one room in a limited number of moves.

```
THESE ARE THE WORDS THE COMPUTER UNDERSTANDS

N,E,S,W : MOVE NORTH/EAST/SOUTH OR WEST
GRAB    : PICK UP TREASURE
PUT     : PUT DOWN TREASURE
LOCATE  : PRINTS CURRENT LOCATION OF TREASURE
HELP    : TELLS YOU HOW TO PLAY THE GAME
```

The screen above shows the commands you can use to play the game and what they mean. You can only input one command each move so you cannot afford to make mistakes.

To make your task harder you are only allowed to carry one box of treasure at a time.

Sample run

1
```
YOU ARE IN ROOM 4
IT IS FOUL AND FOGGY
IT CONTAINS RUBBISH

WHAT DO YOU WANT TO DO ?
? GRAB

O.K. YOU'RE CARRYING THE RUBBISH
```

2
```
YOU ARE STILL IN ROOM 4
WHAT DO YOU WANT TO DO ?
? W

O.K
```

3
```
YOU ARE IN ROOM 7
IT IS SPOOKY AND SCARY
IT CONTAINS COINS

WHAT DO YOU WANT TO DO ?
? PUT

O.K. RUBBISH PLACED IN ROOM 7
```

4
```
YOU ARE STILL IN ROOM 7
WHAT DO YOU WANT TO DO ?
? S

O.K.
```

Writing the program

The diagram on the right is a flow chart. It shows the structure of the program with each main step shown in order going from top to bottom. The instructions below and on the next few pages will guide you through each stage. Do not worry if you are told to jump to different parts of the program out of sequence. If you follow the line numbering suggested, you can be sure of assembling the program in the correct order.

1 Setting up arrays and reading data (lines 100-250)

You need to put all the information shown on the map on the opposite page into the computer's memory. To do this, store it in a number of arrays.

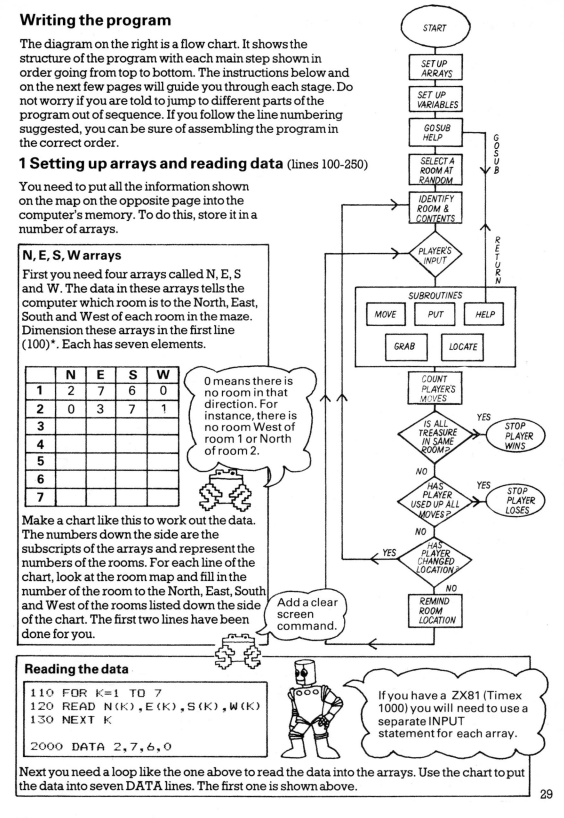

N, E, S, W arrays

First you need four arrays called N, E, S and W. The data in these arrays tells the computer which room is to the North, East, South and West of each room in the maze. Dimension these arrays in the first line (100)*. Each has seven elements.

	N	E	S	W
1	2	7	6	0
2	0	3	7	1
3				
4				
5				
6				
7				

0 means there is no room in that direction. For instance, there is no room West of room 1 or North of room 2.

Make a chart like this to work out the data. The numbers down the side are the subscripts of the arrays and represent the numbers of the rooms. For each line of the chart, look at the room map and fill in the number of the room to the North, East, South and West of the rooms listed down the side of the chart. The first two lines have been done for you.

Add a clear screen command.

Reading the data

```
110 FOR K=1 TO 7
120 READ N(K),E(K),S(K),W(K)
130 NEXT K

2000 DATA 2,7,6,0
```

If you have a ZX81 (Timex 1000) you will need to use a separate INPUT statement for each array.

Next you need a loop like the one above to read the data into the arrays. Use the chart to put the data into seven DATA lines. The first one is shown above.

29

*If you have a ZX81 (Timex 1000) you can only dimension one array per line, so start at line 10.

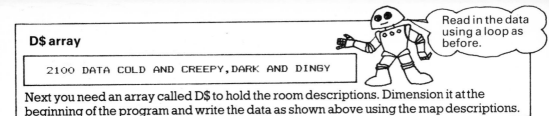

D$ array

```
2100 DATA COLD AND CREEPY,DARK AND DINGY
```

Read in the data using a loop as before.

Next you need an array called D$ to hold the room descriptions. Dimension it at the beginning of the program and write the data as shown above using the map descriptions.

T$ and T arrays

Now you need two more arrays. T$ to hold the names of the treasure and T which tells you where each treasure is. The number stored in each compartment in T is the number of the room where the treasure in the same compartment in T$ is stored. For example at the start of the game, T(2) is 2 and this is the room where treasure T$(2) is stored (the chewing gum). During the game the numbers in T change as the boxes of treasure are moved.

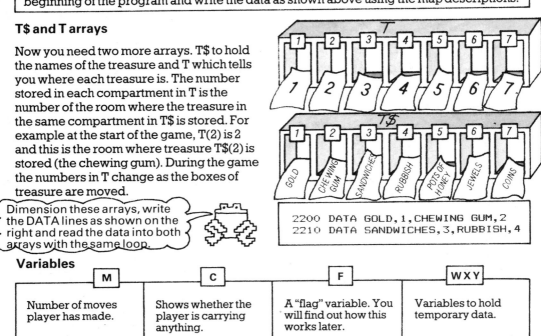

Dimension these arrays, write the DATA lines as shown on the right and read the data into both arrays with the same loop.

```
2200 DATA GOLD,1,CHEWING GUM,2
2210 DATA SANDWICHES,3,RUBBISH,4
```

Variables

M	C	F	W X Y
Number of moves player has made.	Shows whether the player is carrying anything.	A "flag" variable. You will find out how this works later.	Variables to hold temporary data.

The boxes above give the names of the variables you will need later in the program. Starting at line 300, give each of these variables an initial value of 0.

2 Help subroutine (lines 1000-1120)

```
THERE ARE 7 ROOMS IN THE MAZE
AND THERE IS A BOX OF TREASURE
IN EACH ONE. YOU MUST GET ALL
THE TREASURE INTO THE SAME ROOM.
```

Next you need a subroutine to explain the rules of the game. Put a GOSUB command at line 300 and start the subroutine at line 1000. Print the instructions shown on the screen (left) and the commands the computer understands (page 28).

3 Select a room at random (line 350)

The number of the room the player is in is stored in a variable R. To choose a room for the player to start in, make the computer pick a random number between 1 and 7 and store it in R at line 350.

4 Identifying the room and contents (lines 400-470)

```
YOU ARE IN ROOM 7
IT IS SPOOKY AND SCARY
IT CONTAINS : COINS
```

```
YOU ARE IN ROOM 4
IT IS FOUL AND FOGGY
IT CONTAINS : NOTHING
```

```
YOU ARE IN ROOM 1
IT IS COLD AND CREEPY
IT CONTAINS : GOLD
```

First of all tell the player what room he is in. Then describe the room using R as the subscript of D$. The screens above show what your screen should look like.

Identifying the contents of the room

```
430 FOR K=1 TO 7
440 IF T(K)=R THEN PRINT T$(K):
LET F=1
450 NEXT K
460 IF F=0 THEN PRINT "NOTHING"
470 LET F=0
```

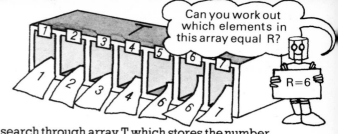

Can you work out which elements in this array equal R?

R=6

To find the contents of room R you have to search through array T which stores the number of the room in which each box of treasure is located. To do this you can use a loop as shown above. The IF/THEN line searches to see whether any of the numbers in T match the room number R. If the numbers match, the computer prints the name of the box of treasure and sets the variable F to 1.

The flag variable

F is 1

F is 0

The F variable tells the computer whether there is any treasure in the room after it has come out of the loop. It works a bit like a flag. When the IF/THEN line is true, the flag goes up (i.e. F is 1) but if it is not true then F stays at 0. Remember to set it back to 0 at line 470 as you will use it again.

5 Player's input (lines 500-560)

WHAT DO YOU WANT TO DO?

Next ask the player what he wants to do followed by an INPUT line which lets the player type a command (such as GRAB, PUT etc.) into a variable A$. Check the player's input by writing five GOSUB lines which will send the computer to a different subroutine for each command. Fill in the line numbers when you have worked out where the subroutines come in the program.

6 Move subroutine

(lines 1200-1260)

Try writing the move subroutine using this flow chart to help you.

1. To move, the player types N, E, S or W, so check which one was typed using four IF/THEN lines.

2. To find the new room number, use R as the subscript of the relevant array (N, E, S or W) and store it in a temporary variable X.

3. Then you must test X to make sure that the player can move in that direction. If X is 0 then there is no room in that direction, so you should print a message and use GOTO to send the computer to the RETURN instruction at the end of the subroutine.

4. If X is not 0, then you should put the new room number into R by making R equal to X.

5. Put RETURN at the end of the subroutine.

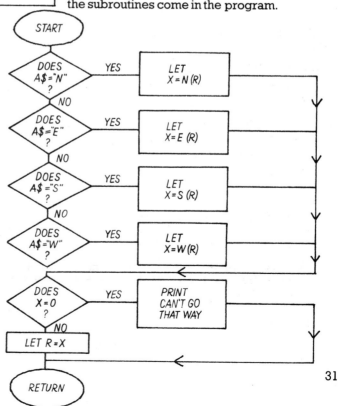

START

DOES A$="N"? — YES → LET X = N (R)
NO ↓

DOES A$="E"? — YES → LET X = E (R)
NO ↓

DOES A$="S"? — YES → LET X = S (R)
NO ↓

DOES A$="W"? — YES → LET X = W (R)
NO ↓

DOES X = 0? — YES → PRINT CAN'T GO THAT WAY
NO ↓

LET R = X

RETURN

31

7 Grab subroutine (lines 1300-1380)

C is 1

C is 0

1. The player can only carry one box of treasure at a time, so first check whether the player is carrying anything. To do this, test the value of variable C, which is set to 1 when the player picks up treasure. If C is 1, print a message and send the computer to RETURN.

R=6 T(7)=6 Y=7

2. To check whether there is any treasure in the room, write a loop using IF/THEN to search through the T array. If a number in T equals the room number (R), then you should store the T subscript number (represented by K) in a temporary variable called Y. As the computer runs through the loop it may find that several numbers equal R. In this case, Y will contain the subscript of the last of these T numbers when the computer has finished the loop.

START

DOES C = 1 ? — YES → YOU CAN'T CARRY ANY MORE

NO

FOR K = 1 TO 7

LOOP

DOES T(K) = R ? — YES → LET Y = K

NO

NEXT K

DOES Y = Ø ? — YES → THERE'S NOTHING IN THIS ROOM

NO

CHANGE VALUE OF T(Y) TO 999

SET Y TO Ø ADD 1 TO C

RETURN

3. If Y is 0, then there is no treasure in the room so you should send the computer to RETURN. Otherwise the subscript number stored in Y tells the computer which box of treasure to pick up. Change the value of T(Y) to 999, a number that shows it is being carried. Set C to 1 and Y back to 0 and put RETURN at the end of the subroutine.

8 Put subroutine (lines 1400-1460)

START

1. First you must check whether the player is carrying anything by testing the value of C.

IS THE PLAYER CARRYING ANYTHING? — NO → NOTHING TO PUT DOWN

YES

FOR K = 1 TO 7

LOOP

DOES T(K) = 999 ? — YES → CHANGE T(K) TO EQUAL R

NO

2. Find which box of treasure is being carried by looking for 999 in the T array.

ADJUST VALUE OF C

RETURN

3. If T(K) is 999 change its value to equal the room (R) and set C to 0 again to show the player is not carrying anything.

4. Add PRINT lines to the routine where you think they are needed and put a RETURN command at the end.

9 Locate subroutine (lines 1500-1590)

This routine gives the player the current location of each box of treasure. See if you can write the program for it from the output shown on the two screens below. Plan it out in a flow chart first.

```
YOU ARE CARRYING : GOLD
CONTENTS OF ROOMS:
   2:CHEWING GUM
   3:SANDWICHES
   4:RUBBISH
   7:POTS OF HONEY
   6:JEWELS
   7:COINS
```

```
YOU ARE CARRYING :  NOTHING
CONTENTS OF ROOMS
   7:GOLD
   7:CHEWING GUM
   7:SANDWICHES
   7:RUBBISH
   7:POTS OF HONEY
   6:JEWELS
   7:COINS
```

First test the value of C to find out whether the player is carrying anything. If he is, send the computer through a loop to find the element in array T that equals 999, then print the name of the box of treasure being carried by selecting the element of array T$ with the same subscript. To print the contents of the rooms, you need another loop which prints their current locations except the box being carried (if there is one).

10 Count the player's moves (line 600)

11 Is all the treasure in the same room? (lines 610-690)

At line 600, add 1 to the variable M to keep count of the number of moves the player uses.

The player wins the game if he has moved all the treasure into the same room. You can work this out by testing the numbers stored in array T because they will all be the same when the treasure is in the same room. To do this, take one element of T, T(1) for example, and store it in a temporary variable called W. Then compare it with all the other numbers stored in T, one by one inside a loop. Use a flag variable to indicate whether they are all the same or not.

12 Has the player used up all his moves? (lines 700-750)

Decide how many moves the player should be allowed. If M is greater than this number then the player loses the game. If this is the case, print a message and stop the program.

13 Has the player changed location? (lines 800-850)

```
YOU ARE STILL IN ROOM 7
WHAT DO YOU WANT TO DO ?
?
```

If the player typed N, E, S or W into A$ at the INPUT line, send the player back to line 400 to identify the new room and its contents. Otherwise, remind him of his location and send the computer back to the INPUT line (500).

Program answers

On the next few pages you will find all the answers to the puzzles and projects in this book. The programs are written in a standard BASIC, so you may have to convert some of the non-standard commands, such as RND and CLS to suit your computer. If one of the programs listed here does not work, first check that your computer uses all the BASIC words in that program. There is a conversion chart on page 47 to help you. Program lines which need major alterations for Sinclair (Timex) computers are marked with △ and the alternative lines are given nearby. Lines which need changing only on the ZX81 (Timex 1000) are marked ▲.

For some of the puzzles you may find that the program you have written is different from the one in the answers. This does not matter so long as your program runs correctly. Study the answer, though, and make sure your program is as short and neat as possible.

Getting to know BASIC (pages 4-5)
Simple program puzzles

1
```
40 PRINT "HELLO ";
50 PRINT A$
```
The semicolon makes the computer stay on the same line to print A$.

2
```
40 PRINT "HELLO",A$
50 Delete this line.
```
The comma makes the computer leave some spaces before printing A$.

3
```
40 PRINT TAB(6);"HELLO ";A$
50 Delete this line.
```
Some computers do not need a semicolon after TAB.

4
```
40 PRINT "          GOODBYE"
50 PRINT "          ";A$
```

Variable puzzles (pages 6-7)
Choosing variable names

These names contain BASIC words and cannot be used as variable names: LETTER$ (LET); RUN$(RUN). The ZX81 (Timex 1000) will only accept one letter string variable names, so you cannot use FLEA$ on that computer either.

PRINT puzzle
```
   10 LET A=66
   20 LET B=77
▲  30 LET RR$="RUSTY ROBOTS"
   40 PRINT A;" ";RR$;" ATE"
   50 PRINT B;" SINGED SAUSAGES"
```
A space inside quotation marks makes the computer print a space.

Looking inside a program
```
45 PRINT "C IS ";C
55 PRINT "D IS ";D
```

Centigrade to Farenheit
```
40 LET C=9/B
50 LET D=C*A
60 LET R=D+F
```
Change lines 40-60 as shown above.

Program writing puzzles

1
```
10 LET U$="UG"
20 PRINT "WHAT IS YOUR WORD "
30 INPUT W$
40 PRINT "THE UGLIAN WORD IS ";
50 PRINT U$;W$
```
Line 50 makes the computer print UG followed by the word stored in W$.

2
```
10 PRINT "WHAT IS THE DISTANCE ";
20 INPUT D
30 PRINT "HOW LONG DID YOU TAKE ";
40 INPUT T
50 LET S=D/T
60 PRINT "YOUR SPEED WAS ";S;
70 PRINT " MILES PER HOUR"
```
At line 50 the computer calculates the speed and stores it in S.*

3
```
   10 LET A=30
   20 LET B=20
   30 LET S=35
   40 LET T=S/B
   50 LET C=A*T
   60 LET D=C+S
   70 PRINT "THEY MUST BUY ";
   80 PRINT D;" SAUSAGES."
   90 PRINT "IT WILL TAKE THEM ";
  100 PRINT T;" HOURS"
```
A and B are the sausages the robots can eat in an hour. S is the sausages Robot 2 wants to eat and T is the time Robot 2 takes to eat his sausages (S). Line 50 works out the number of sausages Robot 1 eats in that time (T) and D is the total number of sausages.

Repeating things (pages 8-9)
Loop puzzles

1
```
10 FOR J=1 TO 100
20 PRINT "HELLO ";
30 NEXT J
```
The semicolon in line 30 makes the computer stay on the same line to print the next word.

2
```
10 FOR J=1 TO 25
20 PRINT TAB(15);"HELLO"
30 NEXT J
```
This makes the computer print a column of 25 HELLOs, 15 spaces from the left of the screen.

*On some computers (e.g. Vic 20 and Pet) leave out the semicolon at the end of PRINT lines before INPUT.

3 Line 20 is wrong because it interferes with the loop counter, I. Each time the loop goes round, line 20 changes the value of I from 1 to 0.

Step puzzles

1
```
10 FOR I=25 TO 1 STEP-1
20 PRINT TAB(I);"HELLO"
30 NEXT I
```

Use the loop variable (I) as the TAB number. Make sure I is not bigger than the width of your screen. Each time the loop repeats, I decreases by 1.

2
```
10 FOR L=5 TO 0 STEP-1
20 PRINT TAB(5);L;TAB(10);L*L
30 NEXT L
```

Step −1 makes the loop variable (L) count backwards from 5 to 0. Each time the loop repeats, line 20 prints the value of L and then squares it.

3
```
10 PRINT "START ";
20 INPUT A
30 PRINT "STOP ";
40 INPUT B
50 PRINT "STEP ";
60 INPUT C
70 FOR J=A TO B STEP C
80 PRINT J;"  ";
90 NEXT J
```

The loop in lines 70-90 uses A to set the initial value of the loop variable, B to set the final value and C for the step.

Secret message
```
10 PRINT "SECRET MESSAGE"
20 PRINT "MEMORIZE IN 5 SECONDS"
30 PRINT "THEN IT WILL DISAPPEAR"
40 PRINT
50 PRINT "MEET AGENT X. 2.00 AIRPORT"
60 FOR I=1 TO 1000 ⎤—Delay loop
70 NEXT I         ⎦
80 CLS ——— Clears screen
```

Pattern puzzles

2
```
50 PRINT TAB(A-K);"*";
60 PRINT TAB(A+K);"*"
70 NEXT K
```

A is the top of the triangle. To print the left side you subtract K from A and to print the right you add K to A.

3
```
30 Delete this line.
40 FOR K=9 TO 1 STEP-1
80 PRINT TAB(A);"*"
```

Change these lines to print the shape upside down. To make the other patterns shown on page 9 use the same program with different TAB positions.

Loop puzzles (pages 10-11)

Loop to make program run more slowly

You could add this nested loop at line 45 or line 55.
```
45 FOR K=1 TO 1000
48 NEXT K
```

Bugs in loops

Lines 50 and 70 are wrong and should read like this:
```
50 NEXT K
70 NEXT I
```

Binary counter

To make a program that counts in eight-figure numbers you need four more loops (E, F, G, H). You will need to renumber the program and alter the PRINT lines like this:
```
PRINT H+G*2+F*4+E*8+D*16+C*32+B*64+
A*128;" = ";
PRINT A;B;C;D;E;F;G;H
```

Flashing message
```
10 FOR J=1 TO 10
20 CLS
30 FOR K=1 TO 1000:NEXT K
40 PRINT TAB(10);"DANGER"
50 PRINT TAB(7);"SPACE ATTACK"
60 FOR K=1 TO 1000:NEXT K
70 NEXT J
```

Here is a program to print a flashing message. You may need to change the size of the delay loop and alter the TAB positions to suit your screen. If your computer does not accept multistatement lines, put the NEXT K command on a new line.

Computer clock
```
10 FOR J=0 TO 59              Minutes
20 FOR K=0 TO 59              loop
30 PRINT J;":";K
40 FOR L=1 TO 500:NEXT L      Seconds
50 CLS                        loop
60 NEXT K
70 NEXT J
```

Set the K loop to make a delay of one second.

Rocket lift off
```
 10 CLS
▲20 FOR I=1 TO 20
 30 PRINT
 40 NEXT I
 50 PRINT "   *   "
 60 PRINT "  ***  "
 70 PRINT "  ***  "
 80 PRINT "  ***  "
 90 PRINT " ** ** "
100 FOR J=1 TO 25
▲110 PRINT
120 FOR K=1 TO 1000 ⎤—Delay loop
130 NEXT K          ⎦
140 NEXT J
```

The loop in lines 20-40 makes the computer print empty lines so the rocket is printed at the bottom of the screen. Lines 50-90 print the rocket shape. You should make the loop in lines 100-140 repeat as many times as the number of rows on your screen. Each time the loop repeats, the computer prints an empty line and the rocket moves one line up the screen.

Sinclair (Timex) changes
To run the program on the Spectrum (Timex 2000), press ENTER when the scroll message appears on the screen.
▲For the ZX81 (Timex 1000), change these lines:
```
 20 FOR I=1 TO 17
110 SCROLL
```

Jumping man program

```
10 FOR J=1 TO 25 STEP 2
20 CLS
30 PRINT
40 PRINT TAB(J);" O "
50 PRINT TAB(J);"<O>"
60 PRINT TAB(J);"/ \"
70 FOR K=1 TO 1000
80 NEXT K
90 CLS
100 PRINT TAB(J+1);"<O>"
110 PRINT TAB(J+1);" O "
120 PRINT TAB(J+1);"/ \"
130 FOR K=1 TO 1000
140 NEXT K
150 NEXT J
```

You should make the loop from lines 10-150 run as many times as the number of characters that fit across your screen. Lines 40-60 print the man in the first position. Lines 70-80 and 130-140 are delay loops to make the man stay on the screen a moment. Lines 100-120 print the man in the second position.

IF/THEN exercises (pages 12-13)

Tables tester

```
55 IF B<>J*A THEN PRINT "WRONG. ";
J;" X ";A;" = ";J*A
```

Add this line to make the computer tell you when your answer is wrong.

Password

```
50 IF P$<>S$ THEN PRINT "WRONG.
THICK HEAD"
60 IF P$=S$ THEN PRINT "O.K. CONTINUE"
```

Add these lines (with your own message) to complete the password program.

```
10 LET S$="SAUSAGES"
20 LET N=007
30 PRINT "PASSWORD PLEASE ";
40 INPUT P$
50 PRINT "SECRET NUMBER ";
60 INPUT SN
70 IF P$<>S$ OR SN<>N THEN PRINT
"WRONG. THICK HEAD"
80 IF P$=S$ AND SN=N THEN PRINT
"O.K. CONTINUE"
```

Change the password program like this to make the computer ask you for a secret number as well.

Computer calculator

```
10 PRINT "THINK OF A NUMBER ";
20 INPUT X
30 PRINT "AND ANOTHER ";
40 INPUT Y
50 PRINT "DO YOU WANT TO :"
60 PRINT "ADD, SUBTRACT, DIVIDE"
70 PRINT "OR MULTIPLY ?"
80 INPUT A$
90 IF A$="ADD" THEN LET A=X+Y
100 IF A$="SUBTRACT" THEN LET A=X-Y
110 IF A$="DIVIDE" THEN LET A=X/Y
120 IF A$="MULTIPLY" THEN LET A=X*Y
130 PRINT "THE ANSWER IS ";A
```

The computer carries out a different sum depending on the answer you input for A$.

Guessing games

```
45 IF Y<X THEN PRINT "TOO SMALL"
46 IF Y>X THEN PRINT "TOO BIG"
```

Add these lines to make the computer tell you when your guess is too big or too small.

```
5 LET N=0
55 LET N=N+1
56 IF N>5 THEN STOP
```

Add these lines to count the number of guesses and stop the program after five.

Word game

```
10 PRINT "WORD PLEASE ";
20 INPUT W$
30 PRINT "CLUE PLEASE ";
40 INPUT C$
50 CLS
60 PRINT "CLUE :";
70 PRINT C$
80 PRINT "GUESS THE WORD"
90 INPUT G$
100 IF G$=W$ THEN GOTO 130
110 PRINT "NO"
120 GOTO 90
130 PRINT "YES"
```

Lines 10-40 make the computer ask for a word and clue.
Lines 50-60 clear the screen and print the clue.
Line 120 sends the computer back to line 90 for another guess.

Horse race

Here are the completed IF/THEN lines for the Horse race game.

```
80 IF G1=H1 AND G2=H2 THEN GOTO 160
90 IF G1=H2 OR G2=H1 THEN GOTO 150
100 IF (G1=H1 AND G2<>H2) OR (G2=H2
AND G1<>H1) THEN GOTO 140
120 IF N=4 THEN GOTO 170
```

Line 80: You should send the computer to line 160 if both guesses are correct.
Line 90: If the horse is correct but the place is wrong, send the computer to line 150.
Line 100: If one guess is correct go to line 140.
Line 120: After four guesses, send the computer to line 170.

Ideas to improve the game

```
15 LET S=0
140 PRINT "ONE CORRECT GUESS":LET
S=2:GOTO 120
160 PRINT "CORRECT:LET S=4
180 PRINT "YOUR SCORE IS ";S
```

Here is an idea for a scoring system that gives four points for guessing both horses and two points for one horse correct. Variable S holds the score.

```
190 PRINT "DO YOU WANT ANOTHER GO ? (Y/N)"
200 INPUT Z$
210 IF Z$="Y" THEN GOTO 10
220 IF Z$="N" THEN STOP
```

To give the player the choice of running the program again, add these lines.

Random numbers (pages 14-15)

Random number between 10 and 20

```
INT(RND(1)*11+10)
```

To do this, multiply by the number of figures in the range (11), then add the first number in the range (10). Use your computer's RND command.

Program puzzle

```
20 LET X=INT(RND(1)*20+1)
```

Change line 20 of the number guessing game to make the computer pick a random number between 1 and 20.

Number sequence

Add these lines to the program for the number sequence game.

```
  5 PRINT "GUESS THE NEXT NUMBER"
  7 PRINT "IN THIS SEQUENCE"
 10 LET X=INT(RND(1)*10+1)
 20 LET Y=INT(RND(1)*10+1)
 60 LET A=X+4*Y
 70 INPUT N
 80 IF N=A THEN PRINT "CORRECT"
 90 IF N<>A THEN PRINT "WRONG. IT'S ";A
100 GOTO 5
```

Line 60 works out the next number in the sequence.

Random sequence

```
24 LET R=INT(RND(1)*3+1)
25 IF R=1 THEN GOTO 30
26 IF R=2 THEN GOTO 40
27 IF R=3 THEN GOTO 50
```

To select a sequence at random make the computer pick a random number between 1 and 3 and store it in R. Send the computer to a different sequence depending on the value of R.

```
30 FOR I=1 TO 3
33 PRINT X+I*I
35 NEXT I
37 LET A=X+4*4
39 GOTO 70
40 FOR I=1 TO 3
43 PRINT I*I-Y
45 NEXT I
47 LET A=4*4-Y
49 GOTO 70
50 FOR I=1 TO 3
53 PRINT X+Y-I*I
55 NEXT I
57 LET A=X+Y-4*4
```

To add three different number sequences to the program, delete lines 30-60 and add a separate loop for each sequence. At the end of the first two sequences, send the computer to line 70.

Escape from Zorgos

```
 10 LET C=10
 20 PRINT "YOU HAVE ";C;" CHIPS"
 30 PRINT "PLACE YOUR BET :";
 40 INPUT B
 50 IF B>C THEN PRINT "YOU HAVEN'T GOT
THAT MANY CHIPS":GOTO 20
 60 LET C=C-B
 70 LET X=INT(RND(1)*6+1)
 80 LET Y=INT(RND(1)*6+1)
 90 PRINT "PRESS P TO THROW :";
100 INPUT P$
110 IF P$<>"P" THEN GOTO 90
120 PRINT TAB(5);X;TAB(10);Y
130 IF X=Y THEN GOTO 250
140 IF X+Y=10 OR X+Y=11 THEN GOTO 210
150 IF X+Y=6 OR X+Y=7 THEN GOTO 190
160 PRINT "SORRY. YOU LOST YOUR BET"
170 IF C=0 THEN GOTO 290
180 GOTO 20
190 PRINT "NO CHANGE. YOU KEEP YOUR BET"
200 LET C=C+B:GOTO 20
210 PRINT "WELL DONE. YOU TRIPLED YOUR BET"
220 LET C=C+(B*3)
230 IF C>=50 THEN GOTO 320
240 GOTO 20
250 PRINT "YOU DOUBLED YOUR BET"
260 LET C=C+(B*2)
270 IF C>=50 THEN GOTO 320
280 GOTO 20
290 PRINT "SORRY. YOU'RE OUT OF CHIPS"
300 PRINT "THERE'S NO ESCAPE FROM ZORGOS"
310 STOP
320 PRINT "WELL DONE. NOW YOU CAN ESCAPE"
330 PRINT "FROM ZORGOS WITH ";C;" CHIPS"
```

C keeps count of number of chips.

Make sure player's bet is not more than the number of chips.

Work out how many chips are left.

Pick two random numbers between 1 and 6.

Check player's input.

Print the random numbers on the screen.

Check the numbers and send computer to different lines to work out different scores.

Check number of chips left. If C=0 send computer to end of program.

Send computer back for another bet.

Adjust value of C.

If C is 50 or more, send computer to end of program.

Paper, Stone, or Scissors: Spot the bugs

Correct the following lines as shown below to make the program run properly.

```
 50 LET R=INT(RND(1)*3+1)
 80 IF R=3 THEN LET C$="SCISSORS"
150 IF C$="SCISSORS" AND A$="STONE"
THEN LET F=1
190 PRINT "SO ";
210 IF F=1 THEN PRINT "YOU WIN"
230 IF F=0 THEN LET C=C+1
240 IF F=1 THEN LET A=A+1
280 IF C<10 AND A<10 THEN GOTO 40
```

Character crunching (pages 16-17)
String puzzles

1 △ `40 PRINT TAB(K);MID$(N$,K,1)`

This makes the computer print one letter from the word at a time, at TAB position K, starting with letter number K.

2
```
 10 LET K$="KANGAROO"
 20 LET L=LEN(K$)
 30 FOR J=L TO 1 STEP-1
```
△ `40 PRINT MID$(K$,J,1);`
```
 50 NEXT J
```

Use a − 1 step loop to make the computer print a word backwards.

3 △ `50 PRINT RIGHT$(S$,L-J)+LEFT$(S$,J)`

Each time the loop repeats, RIGHT$(S$, L-J) makes computer print L (the length of the word) minus J letters from the right of SQUARES, and then add J letters from the left. Try running this program with different words.

Longest word

```
50 IF LEN(W$)>LEN(A$)

THEN LET A$=W$
```

Each time the loop repeats the computer compares the length of W$ with A$. If W$ is longer than A$, it replaces A$ with W$ and then compares the next word. At the end of the loop A$ will contain the longest word entered.

Shortest word

```
10 LET A$="XXX!!!&&ABC***123!!!!
XXXXXXXXXX"
50 IF LEN(W$)<LEN(A$)
THEN LET A$=W$
70 PRINT "SHORTEST WORD :"
```

This is the same as the longest word program except for lines 10 and 50. Line 10 contains a string of characters for the computer to compare the length of each word with. It does not matter what characters you put in A$.

Word editor

Here are the completed program lines from the Word editor program.

```
40 LET S$=" "+S$+" "
70 LET W$=" "+W$+" "
```

You need to add spaces either side of S$ and W$ to make sure in line 140 that the computer only searches for whole words. Without the spaces the computer would pick out any characters in the sentence which matched S$ or W$. Try running the program without these spaces and see what happens.

```
100 LET LS=LEN(S$)
110 LET LW=LEN(W$)
```

These lines make LS equal the length of S$ and LW equal the length of W$. Line 100 is repeated again at line 160 to make LS equal the length of the new sentence.

△ `140 IF MID$(S$,K,LW)=W$`
`    THEN LET A$=S$`

Each time the loop repeats MID$(S$, K, LW) makes the computer check LW (the length of W$) characters in S$, starting at character K. When it finds a sequence of characters which match W$, it stores the whole sentence in a new variable, A$.

△ `150 IF A$=S$ THEN LET S$=LEFT$(A$,K)`
`    +N$+RIGHT$(A$,LS-(K+LW-2))`

LEFT$(A$,K) works out the number of characters to the left of the word you want to replace. The best way to understand how this line works is to try it out with a sentence on a piece of paper.

```
180 IF K<=LS-LW+1 THEN GOTO 140
```

Send the computer back to line 140 to check through the rest of the sentence in case the word you want to replace occurs another time.

Alterations for Sinclair (Timex) computers

String puzzles

Insert these lines in the String puzzle answers 1, 2 and 3.

1 `40 PRINT TAB(K);N$(K TO K)`

2 `40 PRINT K$(J TO J);`

3 `50 PRINT S$(J+1 TO )+S$( TO J)`

Word editor
```
140 IF S$(K TO K+LW-1)=W$ THEN
LET A$=S$
150 IF A$=S$ THEN LET S$=A$( TO K)
+N$+A$(K+LW-1 TO )
```

Replace these lines in the Word editor program.

More character crunching (page 18)

Letter puzzles

1 ▲
```
10 FOR K=65 TO 90
```
These are the ASCII numbers to print out the alphabet. On the ZX81 (Timex 1000), the numbers should be 38 to 63.

2
```
10 FOR K=97 TO 122
20 PRINT CHR$(K);
30 NEXT K
```
These are the numbers to print out the alphabet in small letters. (On some computers, e.g. the Dragon which cannot print small letters, these numbers are used for a different set of capital letters.)

3 ▲
```
10 LET R=INT(RND(1)*26+65)
20 PRINT CHR$(R);
30 GOTO 10
```
This is the simplest way to print a series of random letters. For the ZX81 (Timex 1000), replace 65, the code number for the first letter in the alphabet, with 38.

Comparing letters
```
10 INPUT X$,Y$
20 IF X$<Y$ THEN PRINT X$;" COMES
BEFORE ";Y$
30 IF Y$<X$ THEN PRINT Y$;" COMES
BEFORE ";X$
40 GOTO 10
```
If your computer only allows one variable after INPUT, use two separate INPUT lines.

Capital converter
```
50 IF X$>="a" AND X$<="z" THEN PRINT
CHR$(ASC(X$)-32);
60 IF X$>="A" AND X$<="Z" THEN PRINT
CHR$(ASC(X$)+32);
```
The missing number in lines 50 and 60 is 32. This is the difference between the code numbers of capital and small letters. Have a look at the code chart in your manual.

Code writing programs (page 19)

Secret code writer

Here is the complete program with the missing numbers and symbols filled in. Use this program for the Spectrum (Timex 2000) but change the ASC command to CODE. For the ZX81 (Timex 1000) use the program on the right.
```
   10 PRINT "WHAT IS YOUR MESSAGE"
   20 INPUT M$
   30 FOR J=1 TO LEN(M$)
△  40 LET X=ASC(MID$(M$,J,1))
   50 IF X<65 OR X>90
   THEN LET N=X:GOTO 100
   60 IF INT(J/2)=J/2 THEN LET N=X+1
   70 IF INT(J/2)<>J/2 THEN LET N=X-1
   80 IF N<65 THEN LET N=N+26
   90 IF N>90 THEN LET N=N-26
  100 PRINT CHR$(N);
  110 NEXT J
```

▲ ZX81 (Timex 1000) Secret code writer
```
 10 PRINT "WHAT IS YOUR MESSAGE"
 20 INPUT M$
 30 FOR J=1 TO LEN(M$)
 40 LET X=CODE(M$(J TO J))
 50 IF X<38 OR X>63 THEN LET N=X
 55 IF X<38 OR X>63 THEN GOTO 100
 60 IF INT(J/2)=J/2 THEN LET N=X+1
 70 IF INT(J/2)<>J/2 THEN LET N=X-1
 80 IF N<38 THEN LET N=N+26
 90 IF N>63 THEN LET N=N-26
100 PRINT CHR$(N);
110 NEXT J
```

Lines 60-70 check whether the loop variable J is odd or even by dividing J by 2, then using INT to make it into a whole number. The computer then checks to see if the answer equals J/2 and if it does, J is an even number.

Key number code

For this program use the Secret code writer program and insert lines to input a secret number. Then you need to change line 60 to add the key number (K) to the ASCII code number (X) for each character, and delete line 70.
```
25 PRINT "WHAT IS THE KEY NUMBER"
27 INPUT K
60 LET N=X+K
70 Delete this line.
```

Loopy code

This is also the same as the Secret code writer, but at line 60 you should add the loop variable (J) to the ASCII code number for each character.
```
60 LET N=X+J
70 Delete this line.
```

Loopy code decoder

To write a decoder, change line 60 to read:
```
60 LET N=X-J
```

Reverse code
```
   10 INPUT "MESSAGE ";M$
   20 FOR J=1 TO LEN(M$) STEP 2
△  30 PRINT MID$(M$,J+1,1);
△  40 PRINT MID$(M$,J,1);
   50 NEXT J
```
Step 2 makes the computer count in twos. Each time the loop repeats it prints the second (J+1) of a pair of characters on the screen, followed by the first (J).

Sinclair (Timex) Reverse code changes
```
30 PRINT M$(J+1 TO J+1);
40 PRINT M$(J TO J);
```

39

INKEY$ exercises (pages 20-21)

Use your computer's INKEY$ command.

Printing HELLO

```
10 LET A$=INKEY$
20 IF A$="" THEN PRINT " ";
30 IF A$<>"" THEN PRINT "HELLO";
40 GOTO 10
```

If no key is pressed, A$ is empty and the computer prints a space (line 20). If a key is pressed it is stored in A$ and the computer prints HELLO (line 30).

Making the computer wait

```
10 LET A$=INKEY$
20 IF A$="" THEN GOTO 10
30 Rest of program...
```

Line 20 makes the computer repeat line 10 so long as no key is pressed.

High speed maths bugs

Correct the following lines as shown below to make the program run properly.

```
20 PRINT "PRESS THE KEY WHEN YOU"
```
— Add missing quotes.
```
50 LET X=INT(RND(1)*25+1)
```
— Multiply by 25 and add 1 to get a random number between 1 and 15.
```
80 PRINT X;" + ";Y;" = "
```
— Remove quotes before X.
```
110 LET A$=INKEY$
```
— Variable name must go before INKEY$.
```
140 IF N<50 THEN GOTO 90
```
— N should run from 1 to 50 to give all the possible answers to X+Y.
```
160 FOR K=1 TO 1000:NEXT K
```
— Wrong variable after NEXT.
```
170 GOTO 40
```
— Change line number so that N is set back to 0.
```
190 PRINT "YES. THE ANSWER IS ";X+Y
```
— Put variable names outside quotes.

Car crash game (page 21)

This is the program for the car crash game.

```
10 CLS
20 LET C=5
30 LET L=1
40 LET W=10
50 LET R=L+W
60 IF L<=1 THEN LET N=1
70 IF L>=25 THEN LET N=0
80 IF N=1 THEN LET L=L+1
90 IF N=0 THEN LET L=L-1
100 LET A$=INKEY$
110 IF A$=">" THEN LET C=C+1
120 IF A$="<" THEN LET C=C-1
130 PRINT TAB(L);"!";TAB(C);"*";TAB(R);"!"
140 IF C<=L OR C>=R THEN PRINT "*** CRASH ***"
150 GOTO 50
```

- When L reaches either side of the screen the value of N changes.
- When N is 1, value of L increases by one. When N is 0, value of L decreases by 1.
- These lines let you steer the car.
- Prints road and car.
- Works out if car has crashed.
- Send computer back to line 50 to reset the value of R each time L changes.

Add this delay loop if the program runs too fast.

```
142 FOR K=1 TO 400:NEXT K
```

Alterations for ZX81 (Timex 1000)

Add this line: `125 SCROLL`

On this computer, the program runs better with the scoring system. When you crash you should press CONT to make the computer continue the program.

Scoring system

```
140 IF C<=L OR C>=R THEN GOTO 160
145 IF A$<>"" THEN LET S=S+1
160 PRINT "*** CRASH ***"
170 LET CR=CR+1
180 IF CR<=5 THEN GOTO 20
190 PRINT "END OF GAME"
200 PRINT "YOUR SCORE IS ";S
210 STOP
```

Line 145 gives a point each time you steer the car without crashing. Line 180 stops the program after five crashes. You must give CR (the number of crashes) and S (the score) an initial value of 0 at the beginning of the program.

Making road zig-zag at random

```
75 IF L=5 OR L=10 THEN
LET N=INT(RND(1)*2)
76 IF L=15 OR L=20 THEN
LET N=INT(RND(1)*2)
```

One way to do this is to make the computer choose at random which way to go at certain TAB positions of L. To do this you need to randomly change the value of N when L equals, say, 5, 10, 15 and 20.

40

DATA puzzles (pages 22-23)

Name check

```
50 IF X$="JIM" THEN PRINT "YOUR NAME
ISN'T ON THE LIST":STOP
80 DATA CHARLIE,JEMIMA,DEADEYE DICK
90 DATA SAMPSON,DELILAH,JIM
```

Put your own list of names in DATA lines like this, making sure you put a comma between each name. Put the last name in the list in line 50. If your computer does not accept multiple statement lines, repeat the IF/THEN instruction with STOP on a new line.

Restoring DATA

```
10 FOR J=65 TO 90 ]———— ASCII codes
20 FOR I=1 TO 19 ]———— Number of data items
△ 40 IF LEFT$(N$,1)=CHR$(J) THEN PRINT N$
```

Sinclair (Timex) changes

```
40 IF N$(1 TO 1)=CHR$(J) THEN PRINT N$
```

Spot the bug puzzles

1. The data items contain symbols such as – and / so in line 20 you should change the variable to a string variable, e.g. N$.

2. The GOTO command makes the computer carry on trying to read data after it has come to the end of the data list and you will get a syntax error such as "OUT OF DATA AT LINE 50". To solve this you could use a loop to run as many times as there are data items, or put the last data item in an IF/THEN line as in the Name check program.

Joe's Cafe

```
10 PRINT "WELCOME TO JOE'S CAFE"
20 PRINT "HOW MUCH CAN YOU SPEND"
30 INPUT X
40 PRINT "HERE'S WHAT YOU CAN EAT"
50 PRINT
60 READ Y,Y$
70 IF Y<=X THEN PRINT Y$
80 IF Y$="PEPPERMINT MILKSHAKE" THEN STOP
90 GOTO 60
100 DATA 1.99,FRENCH SNAIL STEW
```

List all the other prices and items on the menu in the DATA lines, ending with PEPPERMINT MILKSHAKE.

Telephone directory

```
10 PRINT "WHOSE TELEPHONE NUMBER"
20 PRINT "DO YOU WANT"
30 PRINT
40 INPUT N$
50 READ X$,Y$ ]——————— Read names into X$ and numbers into Y$.
60 IF N$=X$ THEN GOTO 90 ]——— Goes to line 90 when it finds the name.
70 IF X$="   " THEN PRINT "NAME NOT LISTED":GOTO 100 ]—Put last name in your list in the
80 GOTO 50                                              quotes in this line.
90 PRINT X$;":";Y$
100 PRINT "DO YOU WANT ANOTHER NUMBER"
110 INPUT A$
120 IF A$="YES" THEN GOTO 150
130 IF A$="NO" THEN STOP                    You need this line in case you type
140 PRINT "I DON'T UNDERSTAND":GOTO 110 ]—— something other than yes or no at line 110.
150 RESTORE:GOTO 10 ]————————————— Send computer back to beginning of DATA list.
160 DATA CHIPMUNK,670-5054
170 DATA RUSTY ROBOT,60-14-444 ]—— List the names and numbers like this in the DATA lines.
```

Using arrays (pages 24-25)

Numeric arrays

```
10 DIM N(6)
50 DATA 1066,1216,1485,1603,1665,1959
```

Printing out the data

You need a loop like this to print out the data (remember to renumber the DATA line):

```
50 FOR K=1 TO 6
60 PRINT "N(";K;")  IS  ";N(K)
70 NEXT K
```

This loop prints the elements of the array at random:

```
50 FOR K=1 TO 10
60 LET R=INT(RND(1)*6+1)
70 PRINT N(R),
80 NEXT K
```

String arrays

```
△ 10 DIM N$(5)
20 FOR I=1 TO 5
▲ 30 READ N$(I)
40 NEXT I
50 FOR I=1 TO 5
60 PRINT "N$(";I;")  IS  ";N$(I)
70 NEXT I
80 DATA TONY,CORINNE,JUDY,CHRIS,GABY
```

Sinclair (Timex) changes

```
10 DIM N$(5,7)
▲ 30 INPUT N$(I)
```

Calendar calculator

Fill in the missing lines and variables as follows:

```
△ 10 DIM M$(12),D(12)
▲ 30 READ M$(K),D(K)
70 PRINT M$(N);" HAS ";
80 PRINT D(N);" DAYS"
```

Add the rest of the data lines like this:

```
▲ 90 DATA JANUARY,31
```

Insert these lines to alter the program:

```
50 PRINT "WHAT MONTH"
60 INPUT A$
62 FOR I=1 TO 12
△ 63 IF M$(I)=A$ THEN LET F=I
64 NEXT I
70 PRINT A$;" HAS ";
80 PRINT D(F);" DAYS"
```

Sinclair (Timex) changes

```
10 DIM M$(12,9)
15 DIM D(12)
▲ 30 INPUT M$(K)
▲ 35 INPUT D(K)

63 IF M$(I)( TO LEN(A$))=A$ THEN
LET F=1
```

41

Make up your mind program

```
△ 10 DIM I$(10)
  20 FOR K=1 TO 10
▲ 30 READ I$(K)
  40 NEXT K
  50 PRINT "PICK A NUMBER FROM 1 TO 10"
  60 INPUT N
  70 PRINT "WHY DON'T YOU ";
  80 PRINT I$(N)
  90 PRINT "O.K. ";
 100 INPUT A$
 110 IF A$="YES" THEN STOP
 120 PRINT:GOTO 50
 130 DATA PAINT A PICTURE,READ A BOOK
```

Add your data to line 130

Sinclair (Timex) changes

```
  10 DIM I$(10,? )
▲ 30 INPUT I$(K)
```

Count the number of characters in your longest string and put the figure in the DIM statement.

Random number chart

```
100 FOR K=1 TO 10
110 PRINT K;TAB(4);
120 FOR L=1 TO A(K)
130 PRINT "*";
140 NEXT L
150 PRINT
160 NEXT K
```

Writing subroutines (page 26)

Ice cream survey

```
△ 10 DIM I$(5),N(5)
  20 FOR K=1 TO 5
▲ 30 READ I$(K),N(K)
  40 GOSUB 70
  50 NEXT K
  60 STOP
  70 PRINT I$(K);TAB(11);" ";
  80 FOR L=1 TO N(K)
  90 PRINT "*";
 100 NEXT L
 110 PRINT
 120 RETURN
 130 DATA MELON,16,BANANA,11
 140 DATA GINGER,8,GHERKIN,1
 150 DATA BUBBLE GUM,18
```

You need the TAB instruction in line 70 to make sure the computer prints the *s at the same place on each line.

Sinclair (Timex) changes

```
  10 DIM I$(5,10)
  15 DIM N(5)
▲ 30 INPUT I$(K)
▲ 35 INPUT N(K)
```

Sink the sub

```
200 PRINT "YOU MISSED"
210 PRINT "TRY ";
220 IF B=Y THEN GOTO 250
230 IF B<Y THEN PRINT "NORTH ";
240 IF B>Y THEN PRINT "SOUTH ";
250 IF A=X THEN GOTO 280
260 IF A<X THEN PRINT "EAST"
270 IF A>X THEN PRINT "WEST"
280 RETURN
```

42 This is the subroutine to compare the sub's location with the guess and print a message on the screen.

Twenty questions

```
△ 10 DIM Q$(20),A(20)
  20 FOR K=1 TO 20
▲ 30 READ Q$(K),A(K)
  40 NEXT K
  50 FOR L=1 TO 20
  60 PRINT Q$(L)
  70 INPUT X
  80 IF X=A(L) THEN PRINT "CORRECT"
  90 IF X<>A(L) THEN PRINT "NO STUPID.
THE ANSWER IS ";A(L)
 100 PRINT
 110 NEXT L
 120 DATA HOW MANY LEGS
DOES A CENTIPEDE HAVE ?,100
 130 DATA HOW MANY PLAYERS
IN A FOOTBALL TEAM ?,11
```

If your answers include symbols or letters, put them in a string array.

Put your questions and answers in data lines like this.

Sinclair (Timex) changes

```
  10 DIM Q$(20,?)
  15 DIM A(20)
▲ 30 INPUT Q$(K)
▲ 35 INPUT A(K)
```

Count the number of characters in your longest string and put the figure in the DIM statement.

Fruit machine program

```
△ 10 DIM F$(6)
  20 FOR K=1 TO 6
▲ 30 READ F$(K)
  40 NEXT K
  50 CLS
  60 LET T=10
  70 PRINT "YOU HAVE ";T;" TOKENS"
  80 LET I$=INKEY$
  90 IF I$="" THEN GOTO 80
 100 LET T=T-1
 110 CLS
 120 LET R=INT(RND(1)*6+1)
 130 LET A$=F$(R)
 140 LET R=INT(RND(1)*6+1)
 150 LET B$=F$(R)
 160 LET R=INT(RND(1)*6+1)
 170 LET C$=F$(R)
 180 PRINT
 190 PRINT A$;"   ";B$;"   ";C$
 200 PRINT
 210 IF A$=B$ AND B$=C$ AND
C$="CHERRY" THEN GOSUB 270
 220 IF A$=B$ AND B$=C$ AND
C$<>"CHERRY" THEN GOSUB 310
 230 IF (A$=B$ AND B$<>C$) OR
(A$=C$ AND C$<>B$) OR (B$=C$
AND C$<>A$) THEN GOSUB 350
 240 IF T>0 THEN GOTO 70
 250 PRINT "NO TOKENS LEFT"
 260 STOP
 270 PRINT "3 CHERRIES"
 280 PRINT "YOU WIN THE JACKPOT"
 290 LET T=T+20
 300 RETURN
 310 PRINT "3 OF A KIND"
 320 PRINT "YOU WIN 5 TOKENS"
 330 LET T=T+5
 340 RETURN
 350 PRINT "2 OF A KIND"
 360 PRINT "YOU WIN TWO TOKENS"
 370 LET T=T+2
 380 RETURN
 390 DATA LEMON,CHERRY,MELON
 400 DATA BELL,GRAPE,PLUM
```

Selects three fruits from F$.

Prints fruits.

Lines 210-230 work out what sort of win you have.

1st subroutine

2nd subroutine

3rd subroutine

Sinclair (Timex) changes

```
  10 DIM F$(6,6)
▲ 20 INPUT F$(K)
```

Treasure hunt program (pages 28-33)

Here is the complete program for the treasure hunt game, listed section by section, in the correct order for the program. The alterations for Sinclair (Timex) computers are at the end of the program.

1 Setting up arrays and reading data

```
△ 100 DIM N(7),E(7),S(7),W(7),D$(7),
     T$(7),T(7)
  110 FOR K=1 TO 7
▲ 120 READ N(K),E(K),S(K),W(K)
  130 NEXT K
  140 FOR K=1 TO 7
▲ 150 READ D$(K)
  160 NEXT K
  170 FOR K=1 TO 7
▲ 180 READ T$(K),T(K)
  190 NEXT K
  200 LET M=0
  210 LET C=0
  220 LET F=0
  230 LET W=0
  240 LET X=0
  250 LET Y=0
  260 CLS
```

See line 2000 for the data.

2 Help subroutine

```
300 GOSUB 1000
```

See line 1000 for subroutine.

3 Select a room at random

```
350 LET R=INT(RND(1)*7+1)
```

4 Identifying the room

```
400 PRINT "YOU ARE IN ROOM ";R
410 PRINT "IT IS ";D$(R)
420 PRINT "IT CONTAINS:";
```

Identifying the contents

```
  430 FOR K=1 TO 7
▲ 440 IF T(K)=R THEN PRINT TAB(15);
     T$(K):LET F=1
  450 NEXT K
  460 IF F=0 THEN PRINT TAB(15)"NOTHING"
  470 LET F=0
▲ 480 PRINT:PRINT
```

F is a flag variable. In line 440, the flag "goes up" (F is 1) when one of the numbers in the T array equals the room number (R).

5 Player's input

```
500 PRINT "WHAT DO YOU WANT TO DO "
510 INPUT A$
520 IF A$="HELP" THEN GOSUB 1000
530 IF A$="N" OR A$="E" OR A$="S" OR
A$="W" THEN GOSUB 1200
540 IF A$="GRAB" THEN GOSUB 1300
550 IF A$="PUT" THEN GOSUB 1400
560 IF A$="LOCATE" THEN GOSUB 1500
```

Lines 520 to 560 send the computer to a different subroutine depending on the word the player types into the variable A$ (line 510).

10 Count player's moves

```
600 LET M=M+1
```

11 Is all the the treasure in the same room?

```
610 LET W=T(1)
620 FOR K=2 TO 7
630 IF W<>T(K) THEN LET F=1
640 NEXT K
650 IF F=1 THEN GOTO 690
660 PRINT "WELL DONE. YOU GOT ALL
THE TREASURE"
670 PRINT "INTO ROOM ";R;" IN ";M;"
MOVES"
680 STOP
690 LET F=0
```

In line 610 the number stored in T(1) is put into variable W. Inside the loop (line 630) the computer compares W with all the other numbers stored in array T. If any T number is different to W the computer makes the flag variable (F) equal 1. If all the numbers in the T array are the same as W F stays at 0 which means all the treasure is in the same room.

12 Has the player used up all his moves?

```
700 IF M<=28 THEN GOTO 730
710 PRINT "SORRY. YOU'VE RUN OUT OF
MOVES"
720 STOP
730 PRINT
```

If M is more than 29 the player has run out of moves and so the program stops. You can change the number of moves the player is allowed.

13 Has the player changed location?

```
800 IF A$="N" OR A$="E" OR A$="S" OR
A$="W" THEN GOTO 400
810 PRINT "YOU ARE STILL IN ROOM ";R
850 GOTO 500
```

2 Help subroutine

```
1000 PRINT "THERE ARE SEVEN ROOMS IN
THE MAZE"
1010 PRINT "AND THERE IS A BOX OF
TREASURE"
1020 PRINT "IN EACH ONE. YOU MUST GET
ALL"
1030 PRINT "THE BOXES INTO THE SAME
ROOM"
1040 PRINT
1050 PRINT "THESE ARE THE COMMANDS THE
COMPUTER UNDERSTANDS"
1060 PRINT "HELP     : TELLS YOU HOW
TO PLAY"
1070 PRINT "N,E,S,W : MOVE NORTH,SOUTH,
EAST OR WEST"
1080 PRINT "GRAB     : PICK UP TREASURE"
1090 PRINT "PUT      : PUT DOWN TREASURE"
1100 PRINT "LOCATE   : PRINT CURRENT
LOCATION OF TREASURE"
▲ 1110 PRINT:PRINT
  1120 RETURN
```

The computer tells you how the game works and the words that it understands. Each time the player inputs the word HELP the computer will come to this subroutine.

6 Move subroutine

```
  1200 IF A$="N" THEN LET X=N(R)
  1210 IF A$="E" THEN LET X=E(R)
  1220 IF A$="S" THEN LET X=S(R)
  1230 IF A$="W" THEN LET X=W(R)
▲ 1240 IF X=0 THEN PRINT "CAN'T GO THAT
  WAY":GOTO 1260
  1250 LET R=X
  1260 RETURN
```

In lines 1200-1230 the computer works out which direction the player typed (N, E, S or W). Then it finds the number of the room in that direction using R as the subscript of the relevant array and stores it in X. If X is 0 (line 1240) it means there is no room in that direction.

7 Grab subroutine

```
▲ 1300 IF C=1 THEN PRINT "YOU CAN'T CARRY
  ANY MORE":GOTO 1370
  1310 FOR K=1 TO 7
  1320 IF T(K)=R THEN LET Y=K
  1330 NEXT K
  1340 IF Y=0 THEN PRINT "THIS ROOM IS
  EMPTY"
  1350 LET T(Y)=999
  1360 PRINT "O.K. YOU'RE CARRYING
  THE ";T$(Y)
▲ 1370 LET C=1:LET Y=0
  1380 RETURN
```

In line 1320 the computer compares each number stored in array T with R. If they are equal it takes the subscript number of that T element and stores it in a variable Y. After the loop, the computer uses Y to pick the right element of T and changes its value to 999 (line 1350). If Y is 0 (line 1340) it means the room is empty.

8 Put subroutine

```
▲ 1400 IF C=0 THEN PRINT "YOU'RE NOT
  CARRYING ANYTHING":GOTO 1450
  1410 FOR K=1 TO 7
  1420 IF T(K)=999 THEN PRINT T$(K);
  " PLACED IN ROOM ";R
  1430 IF T(K)=999 THEN LET T(K)=R
  1440 NEXT K
  1450 LET C=0
  1460 RETURN
```

The computer finds the element of T which equals 999 (line 1420). Then it changes its value to R (line 1430).

9 Locate subroutine

```
  1500 PRINT "YOU ARE CARRYING : ";
▲ 1510 IF C=0 THEN PRINT TAB(10);
  "NOTHING":GOTO 1550
  1520 FOR K=1 TO 7
  1530 IF T(K)=999 THEN PRINT
  TAB(10);T$(K)
  1540 NEXT K
  1550 PRINT "CONTENTS OF ROOMS: "
  1560 FOR K=1 TO 7
  1570 IF T(K)<>999 THEN PRINT
  T(K);"   :   ";T$(K)
  1580 NEXT K
  1590 RETURN
```

1 The data

```
▲ 2000 DATA 2,7,6,0
  2010 DATA 0,3,7,1
  2020 DATA 0,0,4,2
  2030 DATA 3,0,5,7
  2040 DATA 7,4,0,6
  2050 DATA 1,5,0,0
  2060 DATA 2,4,5,1
```

This is the data for the N, S, E, W arrays.

```
  2100 DATA COLD AND CREEPY,DARK
  AND DINGY
  2110 DATA GREY AND GHOSTLY,FOUL
  AND FOGGY
  2120 DATA EMPTY AND EERIE,HAUNTED AND
  HORRIBLE,SPOOKY AND SCARY
```

This is the data for D$.

```
  2200 DATA GOLD,1,CHEWING GUM,2
  2210 DATA SANDWICHES,3,RUBBISH,4
  2220 DATA POTS OF HONEY,5,JEWELS,6,
  COINS,7
```

This is the data for T$ and T.

Sinclair (Timex) alterations

No alterations are needed for the Spectrum (Timex 2000) except that the string arrays should be dimensioned as for the ZX81 (Timex 1000). Each DIM statement should be separated by a colon or put on a separate line as for the ZX81 (Timex 1000).

Line 100: Put the DIM statements on separate lines and dimension D$(7,20) and T$(7,23).

Line 120: Insert separate INPUT lines for each array and type in the data when you run the program.

```
  120 INPUT N(K)
  123 INPUT E(K)
  125 INPUT S(K)
  127 INPUT W(K)
```

Line 150: Use INPUT and type in the data when you run the program.

```
  150 INPUT D$(K)
  180 INPUT T$(K)
```

Line 180: Use INPUT for the T$ array and LET for array T so you do not have to input the starting locations of the treasure each time you run the program. Use a new loop from lines 193-197 for the LET statement, like this:

```
  193 FOR K=1 TO 7
  195 LET T(K)=K
  197 NEXT K
```

Line 350: Use your computer's RND command.

```
  350 LET R=INT(RND*7+1)
```

Line 440: Use separate lines and repeat the IF/THEN instruction, like this:

```
  440 IF T(K)=R THEN PRINT TAB(15);T$(K)
  445 IF T(K)=R THEN LET F=1
```

Lines 480 and 1110: Use separate lines.

Lines 1240-1510: Use separate lines and when there is an IF/THEN instruction, repeat it on a new line, e.g:

```
  1240 IF X=0 THEN PRINT "CAN'T GO
  THAT WAY"
  1245 IF X=0 THEN GOTO 1260
```

Line 2000: Remove lines 2000-3000 and add these lines so you do not have to input the data each time you run the program. When you want to play the game again, just type GOTO 2000. (When you press RUN, the computer clears all the variables and arrays.)

```
  2000 PRINT "DO YOU WANT TO PLAY AGAIN"
  2010 INPUT R$
  2020 IF R$="YES" THEN GOTO 193
  2030 IF R$="NO" THEN STOP
  2040 GOTO 2000
```

Guide to BASIC

Here is a list of the BASIC words used in this book, with a short explanation of what each one means. Words marked with an asterisk are not standard on all computers. For these words, look at the conversion chart on page 47 or in your manual to find the right command for your computer.

ABS tells the computer to ignore the plus and minus signs in front of numbers and gives their absolute values. For instance, ABS(−5) is 5.

*ASC converts a character to its ASCII code number. For instance, ASC("A") will give you 65 which is the ASCII code number for the letter A. Sinclair (Timex) computers use CODE instead of ASC.

**CHR$** converts a number into a character according to the code numbers which represent the characters inside the computer. On computers which use the ASCII code, CHR$(65) gives the letter A. On the ZX81 (Timex 1000), which uses different code numbers, CHR$(38) gives you A.

CLS clears the screen.

*CODE is used on Sinclair (Timex) computers instead of ASC, to convert a letter to its code number. The Spectrum (Timex 2000) uses the ASCII code numbers but the ZX81 (Timex 1000) has its own.

*DATA see READ/DATA

*DIM tells the computer how much memory space to put aside for an array. You use the word DIM followed by the name of the array and the number of items it contains. For instance, DIM A(5) means that there are five pieces of information in the array A. With string arrays on Sinclair (Timex) computers, you must also put the number of characters in the longest string, in the DIM statement.

FOR/TO. . .NEXT makes the computer repeat the instructions between the FOR/TO and NEXT lines a certain number of times. This is called a loop.

GOSUB tells the computer to leave the main program and go to a section of the program called a subroutine. GOSUB must be followed by the number of the first line of the subroutine. At the end of the routine, the word RETURN tells the computer to go back to the main program starting at the instruction after the GOSUB command.

GOTO makes the computer jump to the line number following the word GOTO.

IF/THEN tells the computer to make a decision and do something according to the result. After the word IF, there is a condition which the computer must test by comparing pieces of information. If the condition is true, then the computer will carry out the instructions following the word THEN. If the condition is not true, it will ignore them.

***INKEY$** checks the keyboard to see if a key is being pressed. It does not wait for you to press the key like INPUT, nor do you need to use the RETURN key (or ENTER or NEWLINE on different computers). Because computers work so fast, INKEY$ is often used inside a loop. On some computers you have put a number in brackets after INKEY$ which tells the computer how long to wait.

INPUT tells the computer to wait for you to type information into a variable while the program is running. INPUT must be followed by a variable name.

INT is short for integer (a whole number). It turns a real number (a number with figures after the decimal point) into a whole number by ignoring everything after the decimal point. For instance, INT(6.732) will give you 6. With negative numbers it does the same but rounds the number down to the next whole number so that INT(−3.2) will give you −4.

***LEFT$** tells the computer to take a number of characters from the left hand side of the string. For instance, LEFT$(A$,4) tells the computer to take the first four characters from A$. Sinclair (Timex) computers do not use this command.

A string is a sequence of characters, i.e. letters, numbers and symbols.

LEN gives the length of a string, in other words the number of characters (including spaces and punctuation marks) in a string.

LET labels a memory space and puts some information into it.

LIST tells the computer to display the program listing on the screen.

*__MID$__ tells the computer to take a number of characters from a string. For instance MID$(A$,5,2) picks two characters from the variable A$ starting at the fifth letter. Sinclair (Timex) computers do not use this command.

NEXT tells the computer to go back to the beginning of a loop. See FOR/TO . . . NEXT.

NEW tells the computer to delete the program.

PRINT tells the computer to display something on the screen. PRINT by itself makes an empty line.

*__READ/DATA__ tells the computer to look for the items listed in lines starting with the word DATA and put them into the variable or array following the READ instruction.

REM is short for remark and REM statements are used to remind you what different parts of the program do.

RESTORE tells the computer to go back to the beginning of the DATA lines.

RETURN is used at the end of a subroutine to tell the computer to go back to the main program starting at the instruction after the GOSUB command.

*__RIGHT$__ tells the computer to take a number of characters from the right hand side of a string. For instance, RIGHT$(A$,4) tells the computer to pick the last four characters from A$. Sinclair (Timex) computers do not use this command.

*__RND__ tells the computer to pick a random number.

RUN tells the computer to carry out the instructions in a program.

*__SPC__ tells the computer to print a certain number of spaces across the screen. Not all computers use this command.

STEP is used with FOR/TO . . . NEXT loops to tell the computer how often to repeat the loop.

*__TAB__ moves the cursor a certain number of spaces across the screen. It is usually used with PRINT to display something in the middle of the screen. On some computers you can also use TAB to move the cursor a certain number of rows down the screen. On most computers you need to put a semi-colon after TAB.

THEN is used with IF to tell the computer what to do if certain conditions are true. See IF/THEN.

BASIC symbols

*	Multiply
/	Divide
SQR	Find the square root
^	Raise to the power of. It is not standard so look in your manual to find out what symbol your computer uses.
>	Greater than
<	Less than
>=	Greater than or equal to
<=	Less than or equal to
<>	Not equal

Conversion chart

Command used in this book	CLS Clears the screen.	INT (RND (1) *N+1) Picks a whole random number between 1 and N.	INKEY$ Makes the computer wait for you to press a key.
BBC	CLS	RND (N)	INKEY$ (N)
VIC 20/PET	PRINT CHR$ (147)	INT (RND (1) *N+1)	GET X$
DRAGON	CLS	RND (N)	INKEY$
ORIC	CLS	INT (RND (1) *N+1)	KEY$
TRS 80	CLS	INT (RND (O) *N+1)	INKEY$
APPLE	HOME	INT (RND (1) *N+1)	X$=" " IF PEEK (-16384) >127 THEN GET X$
ZX81 TIMEX (1000)	CLS	INT (RND*N+1)	INKEY$
SPECTRUM TIMEX (2000)	CLS	INT (RND*N+1)	INKEY$

Additional conversions for Sinclair (Timex) computers

LEFT$ RIGHT$ MID$	Sinclair (Timex) computers do not handle strings in the same way as other computers. To convert these commands you should count the position of the first and last characters you want to select. Then put these in brackets with the word TO after the string or its variable name as shown in the examples on the right.	LET X$="CHIPMUNK" PRINT X$(1 TO 4) CHIP PRINT X$(5 TO) MUNK PRINT X$(2 TO 4) HIP
ASC	Use CODE instead of ASC. The ZX81 (Timex 1000) has its own code numbers but the Spectrum (Timex 2000) uses the ASCII code.	PRINT CODE ("A")
DIM	To dimension a string array, use DIM followed by two numbers in brackets. The first is the number of data items (strings) in the array and the second is the number of characters in the longest string. In the example on the right, array A$ contains five strings, the longest of which has 12 characters.	DIM A$(5,12)
READ/DATA	The Spectrum (Timex 2000) uses READ/DATA like other computers but the ZX81 (Timex 1000) has no exact equivalent. The best alternative is a series of INPUT statements as shown on the right.	10 FOR K=1 TO 5 20 INPUT A$(K) 30 NEXT K

Index

In this index you will find the names of the puzzles, BASIC words and ideas covered in this book. The page numbers for the puzzles answers are printed in bold.

First published in 1983 by Usborne Publishing Ltd, 20 Garrick Street, London WC2E 9BJ.
© 1983 Usborne Publishing
The name Usborne and the device ⛤ are Trade Marks of Usborne Publishing Ltd. All rights reserved.